Lyndon B. Johnson

Johnson

Young Texan

Illustrated by Fred M. Irvin

Lyndon B. Johnson

Young Texan

By *Thomas Frank Barton*

THE **BOBBS-MERRILL** COMPANY, INC.
A SUBSIDIARY OF HOWARD W. SAMS & CO., INC.
Publishers • INDIANAPOLIS • NEW YORK

To my mother, Martha Gamblin, and father, Frank Douglas,
both dedicated school teachers and inspiring parents

Illustrations

Full pages

Numerous smaller illustrations

Contents

Books by Thomas Frank Barton

JOHN SMITH: JAMESTOWN BOY

LYNDON B. JOHNSON: YOUNG TEXAN

PATRICK HENRY: BOY SPOKESMAN

★ # Lyndon B. Johnson

Young Texan

An Apple from Grandpa

ALL OF A sudden four-year-old Lyndon and his mother, Rebekah, were aroused from sound sleep. They sat up in bed, wondering what was happening out in the barnyard. They heard the mixed cries of numerous animals out there. Everything seemed to be in turmoil.

Brigham Young, Lyndon's pet dog, barked angrily. He ran through the open breezeway that separated the bedrooms from the kitchen and dining room. Outside squawking chickens flew wildly in all directions. Some flew against the breezeway posts with a dull thud.

Both Lyndon and his mother jumped out of

their bed. Lyndon excitedly opened the door to peek out on the breezeway. Brigham Young ran past him like a streak, yelping loudly and digging his toenails into the wooden floor. Two frightened chickens popped by Lyndon through the door into his bedroom.

Before Lyndon's mother could stop him, he stepped out of his bedroom into the breezeway. "Lyndon! Lyndon! Come back," she called to him frantically. "You may get hurt or killed out there in the yard. There may be a wild animal prowling about, trying to catch a chicken or a pig. Come back! Please come back!"

Lyndon was too excited and curious to obey his mother. He was far too young to understand her fear for his safety. He just kept on going and looking.

Moments later, his two-year-old sister, Rebekah, who had been named after her mother, awoke and started to cry. Her mother rushed over to comfort her, but kept calling, "Lyndon, come back. Lyndon, come back!"

By now Lyndon had left the breezeway and was out in the yard. He called back to his mother, "Don't worry, Mama, Bigham is here. He won't let anything hurt me."

Lyndon's father, Sam Johnson, had purchased the dog as a pup, but now he was full grown. He had named the pup Brigham Young because he had admired a group of Mormons who once had lived nearby. Lyndon was too young to pronounce the word, Brigham, clearly. He left out the letter "r" and called the dog Bigham, but the dog answered just the same.

At present, Sam Johnson was away from home on business. Rebekah, his wife, was alone with the two children, Lyndon and little Rebekah. Sam Johnson's parents, Lyndon's grandparents, lived only about a quarter of a mile away, but too far away to call for help.

Usually a good watchdog locates the cause of trouble quickly, but this morning Brigham seemed to be confused. He merely ran around in circles, holding his head high, as if not knowing in which direction to take off.

Out in the yard the noise continued. The chickens kept squawking and running in all directions, looking for places to hide. The pigs let out ear-splitting squeals and ran hither and yon. The squirrels in two pecan trees near the barn kept jumping from limb to limb and scolding frantically. Frightened blue jays in trees near the cabin darted from branch to branch, adding shrill notes of alarm.

Suddenly the confusion died down almost as rapidly as it had started. Brigham stopped running about and came over to join Lyndon. Then Lyndon patted him and said, "You are a good dog, Bigham. What was the matter?"

Brigham pointed his nose up into the air

as if to answer. Lyndon looked up and saw two large hawks soaring overhead. They flew around in circles a few times and disappeared. The barnyard burglar alarm system had kept them from getting a meal at the Johnson farm.

About this time, Lyndon's mother came to the barnyard, carrying young Rebekah. She paused to put her arm around Lyndon's shoulder and asked, "What caused all the trouble?"

"Just two big hawks flying around overhead," replied Lyndon. "They probably wanted to sweep down and steal a chicken or pig. If Papa had been home, he would have shot them."

"Yes, I wish your father didn't have to be away from home so much," said his mother. "I always feel safer when he is here."

Lyndon's father, whose full name was Sam Ealy Johnson, Jr., had grown up on his father's farm nearby. He now traveled widely through the Hill Country of Texas buying and selling livestock. Also, he was active in politics, and had recently served a term as representative to the Texas State Legislature in Austin.

Lyndon's mother, whose maiden name had been Rebekah Baines, had grown up in the city. She had graduated from college and taught school before she had married Sam Ealy Johnson. Living in the country without close neighbors was a new kind of life for her.

When Lyndon and his mother reached the breezeway, she said, "Now go back to your bedroom to get dressed. Shall we eat breakfast first, or do the chores first?"

"Do the chores first," replied Lyndon.

"All right," she answered. "We'll both have to watch little Rebekah to keep her from getting hurt. While I feed the horses, cattle, and hogs, you can feed the chickens. Then, while I milk the cow, you can hold her tail."

"Why do you want me to hold her tail?" asked

Lyndon. "Are you afraid she will switch and hit you while you are milking?"

"No, but I'm afraid she will switch and get her tail in the milk, or knock dirt into the milk," replied his mother. "Then we would have to throw the milk away."

After Lyndon and his mother finished doing the chores, they took Rebekah and went back to the house. Quickly his mother prepared a good breakfast of soft-boiled eggs, fried bacon, and grits, a kind of hominy which many people eat in the South. While they were still eating, Lyndon suddenly asked, "Mama, how many horses do we have altogether?"

"Five," replied his mother.

"How many of them are work horses?" Lyndon asked seriously.

"Four," answered his mother, "all except Old Dan. Your father uses four horses to plow, cultivate crops, and do other work in the fields.

17

He uses Old Dan when he wants to ride him or drive him hitched to a cart or buggy."

"How many chickens have we?" asked Lyndon, still speaking seriously.

"We have twenty-five grown chickens and sixty young chickens," replied his mother. "But why are you asking all these questions?"

"Well, this afternoon I want to go over to visit Grandpa and Grandma Johnson," he explained. "Grandpa Johnson always sits on the front porch and asks me questions. Then, if I can answer them, he gives me an apple."

"Just be careful before you answer," cautioned his mother.

"Oh, I will," said Lyndon. "The last time when I went to see him, he asked me how many horses we have, and I answered five. Next, he asked me how many of them are work horses and I couldn't tell him. I didn't know what work horses were, so I didn't get an apple."

His mother laughed and started to clear away the breakfast dishes. "Suppose you take Brigham and run outside to play. I want to do some baking this forenoon."

An hour or so later Lyndon came back to the kitchen carrying an armload of fruits and nuts, which he had collected in the yard. "Look, Mama," he called proudly. "I have brought you some good things to eat."

His mother came over to the kitchen table to look. "Oh, thank you," she said, reaching down to give him a hug. Then she began to examine different things which he had brought. "What is this?" she asked, pointing.

"That's a bunch of wild grapes," replied Lyndon, proud to be able to answer.

"What is this," asked his mother, reaching over to pick up a nut.

"That's a shelled pecan," replied Lyndon. He pointed to two other pecans on the table. "Here are two more pecans, one with the shell on, and one with the shell half off."

Lyndon and his mother carefully examined all the fruits and nuts and found a few which they couldn't recognize. These Lyndon put to one side and said, "I'll take them with me so I can ask Grandpa what they are."

Before long Lyndon's mother looked up at the clock and noticed that it was time to get dinner. In the farm country where Lyndon grew up, people called the noonday meal dinner. After dinner Lyndon's mother lay down for a while in the bedroom with little Rebekah to help her quiet down for an afternoon nap.

Lyndon took a thick mail-order catalogue and went out into the breezeway, where Brigham was snoozing comfortably on the floor. He stretched out on his stomach and began to look at pictures of various articles in the catalogue. Soon he was snoozing along with the dog.

20

About mid-afternoon when Lyndon awoke, he jumped up and prepared to go to his grandparents' home. He got out an old pillowcase which he used as a traveling bag. Then he stuffed it full of various things he wanted to take along, including one of his primers.

In a few minutes he and Brigham started off down the road toward his grandparents' home. As they came near, Lyndon saw his grandfather rocking and reading on the front porch. Brigham ran ahead and let him know that Lyndon was coming. When his grandfather saw Lyndon, he called cheerfully, "Hello there, my boy."

"Hello, Grandpa," Lyndon called back. "How are you, and how is Grandma?"

"Very well," answered his grandmother, coming out on the porch with a cool glass of milk. "Here, drink this to help you cool off. You must be hot and thirsty from walking."

"Thank you, Grandma," said Lyndon, starting to sip the milk. "It's very hot today. As Papa would say, 'today is a scorcher.'"

"Has your father come home yet from his latest trip?" asked Grandma.

"No," answered Lyndon, "and we're getting anxious to see him."

"How old are you?" suddenly asked his grandfather, as if he didn't know.

"I'm four years old," answered Lyndon.

"That is right," said his grandfather. "You were born August 27, 1908, and you were named Lyndon Baines Johnson. Baines was your mother's family name."

Now, as Lyndon had expected, his grandfather asked him a long series of questions about farm animals, which he answered correctly. Then his grandfather said, "You have answered well today. I am proud of you."

"Would you like to hear me read?" asked Lyndon, taking his primer from the pillowcase.

"I surely would, pardner," replied his grandfather, "but first let us go inside to see whether I can find something for you."

Lyndon excitedly followed his grandfather into the house and watched him open the lid of his desk. Inside he caught a glimpse of the biggest apple he had ever seen. He knew at once that the apple was for him. "Yes, sure enough,"

said his grandfather, reaching into the desk. "There's something here for you."

"Oh, thank you, Grandpa," said Lyndon, trying to hold the apple with both hands.

Later that day his grandfather wrote a letter to one of his relatives. "Lyndon Johnson, my grandson, is a very intelligent boy," he proudly explained. "He is bright and learns quickly. I predict that he will be a United States Senator when he is forty years old."

By the time Lyndon reached home, it was turning dark. "Where have you been?" asked his mother. "I have been alarmed about you."

"Oh, I have been having a good time talking with Grandpa," said Lyndon. "I answered all his questions about our farm animals, and he gave me a big apple to eat."

"Well, let's go out to the well to get a bucket of water," said his mother.

As she pumped the water in the semi-darkness, she noticed flashes of lightning and heard the rumbles of thunder in the distance. Nearby she heard the shrill calls of whipporwills and the eerie sounds of katydids. "Oh, how I wish your father were home tonight," she said. "Everything seems so frightening."

Suddenly, as she turned from the well with the bucket of water, a screech owl let out a scream directly above her in a tree. She was so startled that she jumped back and let loose of the bucket of water. "Oh, my!" she cried. "What a frightening sound!"

Lyndon helped his mother pump another bucket of water. On the way to the house he took her hand and said, "Don't be afraid, Mama. I will take care of you."

Too Many Pranks

When Lyndon was four and one-half years old, his parents moved to the small town of Johnson City, about twelve miles to the east. This town had been named after a prominent distant relative of Lyndon's father. It was supposed to have a better school for Lyndon to attend while he was growing up.

Lyndon missed doing many things which he had been able to do on the farm. He missed sauntering through the fields with his dog, Brigham. He missed walking up the road to visit his grandfather and grandmother. He just couldn't find enough things to do to keep busy.

The same was true when he started to school. He learned easily and didn't have enough work to keep him busy. This led him to break some of the rules and to play pranks on other pupils. One day he brought his report card home, showing a grade of only C in deportment. His parents were surprised, but said nothing.

A few mornings later, when he awoke from sleeping on a screened-in back porch, he overheard his parents talking about him in the nearby kitchen. He listened closely, because he could tell they were greatly worried about him. "Lyndon must be mischievous in school to get such a low grade in deportment," said his mother. "Do you think we should punish him?"

"No," replied his father. "He just doesn't have enough work in school to keep him busy. If he had more to do, he wouldn't have time to break the rules and play pranks. He is a bright boy and can do more than most children."

"Well, I went over to school to talk with his teacher yesterday," explained his mother. "She said that he learns easily and finishes studying his lessons quickly. When he hasn't anything to do, he becomes restless, so she gives him extra tasks to keep him busy."

"That's good," said his father. "He needs to be kept busy."

"She told me something else about him that I don't quite understand," continued his mother. "She feared that he has become a loner from living on the farm."

"Now, Rebekah, don't be worried about him becoming a loner," replied his father. "We all need to get off by ourselves at times to enjoy nature and to think. Getting alone to think once in a while doesn't mean that we don't like to associate with people. We Johnsons like to get off by ourselves to think, but we also like to associate with our relatives and friends."

28

"I suppose you are right, Sam," replied Lyndon's mother. "Your father certainly was a loner with plenty of time to think in his younger days, when he drove cattle north to Kansas. He must have led a lonely life sitting in the saddle all the way there and back. Yet, today everyone talks about how friendly he is."

"Yes, in many ways Lyndon is like my father," replied Lyndon's father. "I'm proud of him for being so active and intelligent."

"So am I," said Lyndon's mother, "but I think he needs more social life during his younger years. What would you think of enrolling him in Mrs. Glidden's dancing class, which meets every Saturday forenoon? There he would associate with a fine group of boys and girls."

At first Lyndon's father didn't answer, and Lyndon almost fainted. He wanted to shout, "No! No!" but realized that he had to remain quiet and pretend he was still asleep.

"Now, Sam, before you object, let me explain," continued his mother. "Lyndon can learn good manners by attending this dancing school. Besides he can learn how to get along with others under relaxed conditions."

Lyndon's father readily agreed. "As usual, you are right, Rebekah," he said. "Telephone Mrs. Glidden and make arrangements to enroll Lyndon in her school."

Moments later Lyndon's father pushed back his chair and said, "Now I must jump on my horse and ride over toward Fredericksburg to see a farmer about buying some cattle. I promised him that I would come to see him today."

After Lyndon was certain that his father had departed, he pretended to wake up. He stretched, groaned, and rattled the bed, just as he usually did when he awoke. Then he dressed and walked into the kitchen for breakfast. "Good morning, Mama," he said cheerfully.

"Good morning, Lyndon," answered his mother, starting to fry an egg for his breakfast. "Did you have a good night's rest?"

"I surely did," replied Lyndon. "I slept like a log all night long. I didn't wake up until a few minutes ago."

"Good," said his mother. "Your father and I have already had breakfast and he has left on a trip. While he and I were eating, we had a little talk about you. We decided that it would be good for you to join Mrs. Glidden's dancing class, which meets every Saturday forenoon. There you will have a chance to associate with some of the pupils from your school and others whom you don't know."

Lyndon made no response. He just looked at her wide-eyed as if he was greatly surprised. Besides he knew that there was no use to object.

Later that morning Lyndon's mother called Mrs. Glidden and arranged for him to join her

class the following Saturday forenoon. At first, much to his surprise, he enjoyed being there. He liked to take part in the exercises and dances. He had fun visiting with the other children.

One week later, after the excitement had worn off, he began to be bored. He noted sadly that there were more girls than boys in the class and that they giggled almost constantly. He tried to tell them about wild animals which he had seen, but they seemed to be interested only in dogs and cats. He tried to talk with some of the boys, but they weren't interested in wild animals either.

After he made this discovery, he started to talk with the children about their relatives. He asked them questions about their parents, grandparents, uncles, aunts, and cousins, but they barely answered him. Finally, after making several attempts, he completely gave up trying to talk with them.

Occasionally, for want of something else to do, Lyndon teased the other children in the class. He quietly slipped up behind the boys and frightened them by loudly imitating the bark of a fox, or the caw of a crow. He tormented the girls by slyly putting pebbles or grains of wheat into their dancing shoes.

Soon Mrs. Glidden became greatly disturbed by Lyndon's pranks, but she hesitated to scold him or to complain to his parents. Then, one day, when he heard two girls talking about him, he started to get completely out of hand. "Lyndon tells tall stories," said a girl.

"I know," replied the other girl. "Doubtless you have heard him tell that tall story about his grandfather driving cattle from Texas way up north to Kansas."

"Yes, I have," replied the first girl. "My little brother tells tall stories, too."

Angrily Lyndon walked over to the two girls

and grabbed their braids of hair. "I'm telling the actual truth about my grandfather," he shouted. "He made trip after trip and drove thousands of cattle north to Kansas. Ask any cattleman in Texas and he'll tell you."

While this outbreak was taking place, Mrs. Glidden had been in the kitchen. She had gone there to prepare cold lemonade for the children to drink before they left for home. When she came back to serve the lemonade, nobody told her what had taken place.

During the coming week, the two girls studied ways of getting even with Lyndon. Finally they decided to revise a Mother Goose rhyme, called The Donkey, to make it apply to him. This nursery rhyme read as follows:

Donkey, donkey, old and gray,
Ope your mouth and gently bray.
Lift your ears and blow your horn
To wake the world this sleepy morn.

The girls changed the rhyme to read:

Donkey, donkey, young and gay,
Open your mouth and shrilly bray.
Lift your jack rabbit ears and blow your horn
To wake all Johnson City this sunny morn.

During the next Saturday forenoon, the girls watched for a good opportunity to repeat their revised rhyme. Before long Mrs. Glidden went to the kitchen to prepare lemonade for the children to drink during their rest period. At once Lyndon started to tease the children, and the two girls decided that now was the time to act. One girl said to the other, "Do you know that Mother Goose rhyme named, 'The Donkey'?"

"No, not really," replied the second girl. "How does it go?"

Happily the first girl recited the rhyme just as they had changed it to apply to Lyndon. All the children roared with laughter, except Lyndon, whose face was red with anger. He jumped up and shouted, "You all have heard of the Deer Creek Indian battle which took place near here. Let me show you how an Indian scalps someone. I'll pretend I'm an Indian."

He ran over to the girl who had recited the rhyme and started to yank her braids of hair. She screamed with fright and Mrs. Glidden came rushing in from the kitchen. "Stop picking on her, Lyndon Johnson," she called angrily. "Now come to the kitchen with me to help me finish preparing the lemonade."

It took somewhat longer than usual for Mrs. Glidden to bring the lemonade. Lyndon was very quiet the rest of the forenoon, and this was the last dancing class he attended. Years later, Mrs. Glidden confessed that she gave him a spanking after taking him to the kitchen.

Riding
a Mexican Burro

"HEE HAW! Hee Haw! Hee Haw!" brayed a small Mexican burro. He shook his head angrily and flipped his long ears in defiance. He pawed the ground first with one front hoof, and then with the other. In burro language these actions meant, "Which one of you wants to try to ride me again? I defy you to come and try."

Lyndon and two of his friends, Milt and Louis, had been trying to ride this burro. One after another, he had thrown them off about as fast as they had mounted him. Sometimes, when they had climbed on his back, he had bucked up and swayed sideways to throw them off. At other times he had reared up on his hind legs, causing them to slide off backwards. At still other times, he had stood on his front legs with his hind legs up, causing them to slide off over his head. Repeatedly he had outsmarted them, and now they didn't know what to do next.

The stubborn little burro belonged to Milt's father, who was the only physician in Johnson City. Lyndon and Louis were now at Milt's home, hoping somehow to conquer the burro. "Where did your father get him?" asked Lyndon, while they were resting.

"It's a strange story," replied Milt. "A few Mexican sheep herders came through Johnson City driving a herd of sheep. The one who was riding this burro became sick and stopped at my father's office to get some medicine. Soon he felt better, so he offered to give him the burro. My father told him to forget the pay, but he was so grateful that he left the burro anyhow. He tied him in front of my father's office and went on his way. Then my father brought him home and we have had him ever since."

"Possibly he only understands Mexican words and doesn't understand English words," said Lyndon. "Maybe if we could speak to him in Mexican, he would quiet down."

"I doubt it," said Louis. "He should understand by the way we treat him that we want to be friendly with him. We pat his shoulders and stroke his head and mane. We even feed him carrots sometimes."

"Possibly he doesn't like the way we dress," suggested Lyndon. "Maybe if we would wear big Mexican hats, he would let us ride him, but right now I have another bright idea for staying on him. You hold his head while I climb on him and wrap my legs tightly around him. Then I think I can stay on."

Milt and Louis held the burro's head and

Lyndon started to climb on his back. He stood perfectly quiet until the boys let loose of his head. Then all at once he exploded. He jumped, bucked, kicked, and tossed Lyndon high in the air off to one side. As Lyndon slid along on the ground, his over-alls caught on an exposed root of a tree. This root tore a long slit in his overalls and, worse still, cut a deep gash in his leg. Blood poured from the gash.

This accident suddenly ended the riding party for the day. Lyndon wrapped and tied a big red handkerchief around his leg to stop the bleeding. Then he started off limping slowly and painfully toward home, and Milt and Louis led the now docile burro back to the barn.

When Lyndon reached home, he walked around the house to the back yard instead of entering the front door. He intended to wash his leg at the well and go to the barn to get some turpentine to put on the cut. He knew that his father often took turpentine from a big bottle there to put on animals with cuts and bruises. Unfortunately, just as he started to wash off the blood, his mother looked out and cried, "Lyndon, what has happened to you?"

"Nothing much," replied Lyndon calmly.

"Oh yes, there has," said his mother, rushing from the house. "Your overalls are torn and your leg has a big gash in it. Have you been trying to ride that Mexican burro again? If you keep on, you're likely to get some broken bones."

"Don't worry, Mama," said Lyndon. "That burro isn't big enough to hurt anybody."

"Well, he's certainly big enough to throw you and cut your leg," said his mother.

Lyndon started off toward the barn. "While I'm out here, I'll go on to the barn to feed the horses," he said. He actually fed the horses, but they had to wait until after he put turpentine on his injured leg.

The next day was Sunday. Sam Johnson and his family drove over to Grandfather and Grandmother Johnson's home for a picnic dinner. Besides Lyndon and Rebekah, the family now included a younger brother, Sam Houston, and two younger sisters, Josepha and Lucia. All the children enjoyed spending the day with their grandparents, uncles, aunts, and cousins.

After the noonday meal, while the older folks visited, Lyndon had a short chat with his grandfather. "Grandpa," he asked, "have you ever ridden a burro?"

"Yes, a few times," answered his grandfather. "Your mother says that you have been trying to ride one. How are you getting along?"

"Not very well," replied Lyndon. "This burro is perfectly quiet while my friends hold his head, but once I get on his back and they quit holding him, he goes crazy. He bucks and kicks and wham! I find myself on the ground."

"Probably someone has taught him to buck and kick to throw his riders," said his grandfather. "With your good wits and long legs, however, you should be able to ride him."

Lyndon looked his grandfather straight in the eye and said sadly, "Well, so far I have completely failed. Yesterday, in order to stay on, I wrapped my legs tightly around him, and he threw me higher than a kite."

"That was the wrong thing to do," said his grandfather. "The tighter you sit on his back, the easier it is for him to throw you. Just try to sit relaxed on his back. Then, if he tries to throw you to the right or the left, catch yourself with your outside foot and shove yourself right back on him again. If he rises up and tries to throw you forward or backward, catch yourself with both your feet and do the same thing."

"Lyndon," called several of his cousins, "stop talking and come to play ball with us."

44

"Good luck with your riding," called his grandfather. "Remember to relax."

The next morning Lyndon looked at his injured leg and found it much better. Quickly he dressed and went down to the kitchen for breakfast. While he was eating, his mother asked, "What do you plan to do this morning?"

"If you don't mind, I would like to go over to play with Milt and any other kids who come by," he replied.

"Well, I just hope you'll stay away from that pesky burro," cautioned his mother.

After Lyndon reached the street, he made a beeline for Milt's home. Several other boys joined him, guessing that he would try to ride the burro again. "Hold his head, boys," said Lyndon, mounting the burro and letting his legs hang loosely. "Now let go of his head!"

The burro went through his usual tricks. He lurched to one side, but Lyndon knew what to

do. When his foot hit the ground, he shoved himself right back up on the burro's back. Next the burro reared up on his hind legs. Lyndon slid off behind the burro but almost instantly he pushed himself upward and forward on the burro's back again. Moments later, the burro surprised Lyndon by rearing upon his front feet and throwing Lyndon off in front of him.

Lyndon landed on his feet, but he was too surprised to shove himself back up over the burro's head. He merely stood speechless, his face red with anger. Finally he managed to say, "At least he didn't throw me completely. I landed on my feet. Hold his head while I climb on him again. This time I'll show him."

Like all burros, this burro was a smart animal. He noted a tone of determination in Lyndon's voice, which led him to weaken. He half-heartedly pulled a few more tricks but soon gave up and walked off peacefully with Lyndon astride.

At once Lyndon became a hero with the other boys. They shouted gleefully to cheer him. "See how peacefully he rides," they cried. "He completely conquered that stubborn burro."

After Lyndon had ridden the burro a few times around a circle, he jumped off and offered to let the other boys try to ride him. The burro seemed to understand and threw them off as quickly as ever.

"Aw shucks," said Louis, "we might as well give up. That critter is just as mean as ever."

Later on, at Lyndon's suggestion, the boys worked up a plan to earn money with the burro. They decided to take him to the baseball games in Johnson City and charge persons ten cents for trying to ride him.

Soon the burro became an attraction at all the ball games. The spectators howled with glee as they watched him throw one person after another. Then, when everybody had given up,

Lyndon would climb on his back and ride him peacefully. Usually this demonstration made all the others want to try riding him again.

The burro exhibition helped greatly to swell the attendance at ball games. Some came to watch persons try to ride the burro as much as they came to watch persons play baseball. The venture proved to be so successful that the boys soon decided to raise the price to fifteen cents, and about a year later they raised it to a quarter. All the while Lyndon was one of the few persons who could ride the burro peacefully.

Exciting Times at Baptizin' Hole

"WHAT SHALL we do this afternoon?" Lyndon asked a group of neighbor boys who were loafing in the shade of a pecan tree near his home. "Do you have any special ideas?"

"Yes, I have," said Otto, who was noted for coming up with wild suggestions of things to do. "If one of us happens to have a big brother with an automobile, we might get him to take us on a spin over to Fredericksburg. That kind of trip would be fun."

"What a crazy idea!" said one of the boys.

"Are you loony?" asked another. "Why should we want to go to Fredericksburg?"

50

At once Otto's suggestion led to an argument about which was the better town, Fredericksburg or Johnson City. "Fredericksburg is five times larger than Johnson City," said one boy. "It has larger and better stores, where you can buy all sorts of things that the stores here don't even sell."

"Of course," said Otto, picking up the conversation. "Fredericksburg also has electric lights and Johnson City doesn't. It has a railroad and Johnson City doesn't."

"Well, Johnson City may not have a railroad but it has trains," said a boy, coming to the defense of his home town.

"Yes, but our trains are only mule trains, or carts and wagons pulled by mules," said Otto. "They just travel together for safety."

"That may be, but they are important," said another supporter. "They bring food, clothing, and many other things that we need."

"Sometimes they bring livestock to market, and that's certainly important," said still another supporter. "Lyndon knows how important it is because his father is a stockbuyer. He travels all through the Hill Country of Texas to buy livestock."

Lyndon readily agreed, but he was eager to end the argument. "Why argue about which is the better town, Fredericksburg or Johnson City, when we can't do anything about it?" he asked. "Surely we can think of something to do besides arguing."

"Let's play some sort of quiet game," said Otto. "I'm still exhausted from picking bugs from potato plants this morning. The sun almost blistered my bare back."

"I know," said Lyndon. "I picked bugs from potato plants this morning, too. The fumes from the kerosene which I poured on the bugs to kill them almost knocked me out."

For a few minutes there was perfect silence while all the boys tried to think of something to play. Finally Lyndon asked, "How about playing a game of dominoes?"

"Oh, no," cried Otto, "dominoes is an old man's game. If you want to play dominoes, just go over and join the old men at the courthouse. They sit there and play all day long."

"How about playing marbles?" asked Lyndon, pulling a handful of marbles from his pocket.

Nearly all the boys were opposed to playing marbles. One after another, they made such remarks as, "No, you're too good at marbles. You always win. We wouldn't have a chance."

By now Lyndon was losing his patience. He arose and said, "Well, since we can't decide on anything, I think I'll go over to see Milt. Maybe if he can get his father's horse and buggy we can go swimming in the Pedernales River."

"Golly," cried Otto. "That would be great."

Soon after Lyndon left, Otto and the other boys decided that they would like to go swimming, too. They jumped up from the ground and started to follow him. Just as he reached Milt's house, they managed to catch up with him. "Hey, Lyndon," called Otto, "we want to go swimming, too."

Lyndon knocked, and Milt's mother came to the door. "Is Milt here?" he said. "We are trying to organize a swimming party."

Milt's mother called to him. "Lyndon is here with some of his friends," she explained. "He wants to know whether you would like to go swimming with them this afternoon."

"I surely would," said Milt, rushing out to join the group.

"Can you get your father's horse and buggy to drive over to the Pedernales River?" asked Lyndon. "We can't all ride at once, but we can take turns riding and walking."

"No, my father is using his horse and buggy to call on sick people," replied Milt, "but we can hitch the burro to a cart. He is perfectly gentle when he is hitched to a carriage."

Lyndon helped Milt hitch the burro to the cart, and the boys started for the Pedernales River, some riding and some walking. Frequently they stopped to change places from walking to riding. The day was so hot that they were too exhausted to talk.

When they were about half way to the river, trouble arose. The iron rim on the right wheel of the cart started to slip off. Suddenly one of the boys called, "Milt, stop! There's something wrong with the right wheel!"

Milt pulled on the lines and brought the burro to a stop. Lyndon walked around and looked at the loose rim. Then, without saying a word, he picked up a large stone from the roadside and hammered it back in place.

Milt started to drive on, but a short distance farther along the road, the rim came loose again. This time it almost came completely off the wheel. "We might as well go back home," said one of the boys. "We'll never reach the river in time to go swimming."

Once more Lyndon came to the rescue. He picked up a rock and pounded the rim back on the wheel. Then he fastened it on the felloe, or wooden circular part of the wheel, with pieces of wire which he found in the cart. The other boys, amazed by his knowledge and ability, stood and watched him as he worked. Every once in a while, one of them would ask, "Aren't you about finished, Lyndon?"

"Not yet," he replied. "I want to be sure that the rim won't come loose again."

Soon the boys continued their journey and everything went well the rest of the way. The boys shouted with glee when they caught their first sight of the river. Even the little burro, sensing there was good water ahead, started to move along faster.

At first, the boys, eager to cool off rapidly, plunged into a deep section of the river, called Baptizin' Hole. Later, they waded around in shallow water at the edge of the hole, looking for frogs and other small kinds of animals. Finally they sat down on a sand bar to rest and to talk. "Why do people call this deep place in the river, 'Baptizin' Hole'?" asked one of the boys curiously.

Lyndon explained that the deep place was called 'Baptizin' Hole' because Baptist churches often baptized persons here who wanted to become members. "Certain churches require persons to be put completely under water instead of merely having water sprinkled on their heads," he added. "The preacher takes each person out there and puts him under water."

"Do they go into the hole in their best Sunday clothes?" asked another boy.

"Yes," replied Lyndon. "The preacher always is fully clothed and the person he baptizes is fully clothed."

"What keeps the person from getting water in his lungs?" asked still another boy.

"He keeps his mouth shut and tries to hold his breath," replied Lyndon.

"How do you happen to know so much about baptizing?" asked several boys together.

"Because we've always had Baptist preachers in my mother's family," replied Lyndon. "One even baptized General Sam Houston."

Several boys said that they wished they could see a baptismal ceremony. "Why don't you pretend you are a preacher and baptize me to show us what takes place?" asked Otto.

Lyndon readily consented but said that he would need another boy to help him. He chose

Tom because he had seen baptism ceremonies and would know what to do. The two boys, holding Otto by the hands, slowly led him out into the deep water. They stood quietly in the water for a few minutes while Lyndon pretended to conduct the religious part of the

services. Then he and Tom started to swing Otto backward under the water. Suddenly something went wrong. Lyndon and Tom lost their footing and went splashing into the water with Otto. All three boys disappeared, but soon rose to the surface again, and swam over to join the other boys on the bank.

As the three boys relaxed on the bank, they tried to figure out what had happened. Lyndon and Tom reasoned that Otto had struggled with fright and kicked their feet out from under them. "We were standing all right until we swung you back under water," they said.

"Well, you were better off than I was," said Otto. "I couldn't help myself, because you were holding both my hands."

All the other boys leaned back and roared with laughter. "What a baptizing ceremony you put on," they cried. "You baptized three persons at once, even including the preacher."

Advertising
a Shoeshine Boy

ABOUT MIDAFTERNOON one day Lyndon dashed home from downtown Johnson City. "Mama, Mama!" he called as he sat down in the living room to catch his breath.

Quietly his mother stepped out of a bedroom door and said, "Hush! Lucia is just starting to take her afternoon nap. What has happened to make you so excited?"

Lyndon could hardly wait to explain. "You could never guess," he replied. "I ran all the way home to tell you. Papa has bought the newspaper here in Johnson City. He is going to print and sell the newspaper here."

"What?" exclaimed his mother. "Are you sure? I can scarcely believe it."

"Yes, I'm sure," replied Lyndon. "Papa is down at the newspaper office now, and he'll tell you all about it when he comes home for supper tonight."

"Of course," said his mother, "but this is such a surprise. Besides, your father has so many other things to do, I don't know how he'll find time to run a newspaper. We'll just have to wait until he comes home to find out why he made this sudden decision."

She sat down briefly in a chair to rest and to think. A few minutes later, she asked, "Are you hungry, Lyndon? How would you like a mid-afternoon snack of pinto beans and corn bread with sorghum molasses?"

"Oh good!" cried Lyndon. "Right now I can't think of anything better to eat than pinto beans and corn bread with sorghum molasses."

Lyndon went out to the woodpile to get some sticks of cedar wood for the fireplace. Rebekah, Sam Houston, and Lucia streamed along with him. "All of you stop to wash your hands before you come inside," he said.

He paused briefly with the wood to watch the other children. "Rebekah, since you are the oldest, you can get some water from the rain barrel," he said. "Make sure that both Sam Houston and Josepha use soap when they wash their hands. See that Josepha gets her hands clean before she wipes them on a towel."

Lyndon's mother watched and listened from inside the house. He was only nine years old, but he helped her to take care of the younger children. "He makes a good head of the family when his father is away," she thought.

When he stepped into the living room, his mother took an iron poker and lifted a half-burned cedar stick from the ashes in the fireplace. She fanned it briefly with a dustpan until it burst into flames. Then she took the sticks from Lyndon's arms and placed them alongside and on top of the burning stick. Soon all the sticks started to crackle and burn.

By now the younger children were waiting with clean hands for something to eat. Their mother prepared plates of pinto beans and slices of corn bread covered with thick sorghum molasses for all the children. She obtained the beans from a large iron kettle, which hung from a swinging iron arm in the fireplace. She kept beans in the iron kettle all day long, so she could serve them quickly, whenever any of the children became hungry.

While the children sat at the kitchen table, they asked Lyndon about his new job as shoeshine boy at the barber shop in Johnson City. "How much do you get for shining a pair of shoes?" asked his brother, Sam Houston.

"I get ten cents for shining an ordinary pair, like most people wear everyday," replied Lyndon, "but I get more for shining Sunday shoes and cowboy boots."

"Why did you come home so early today?" asked Rebekah. "Weren't you very busy at the barber shop? Usually you don't get home until later in the afternoon."

"No," replied Lyndon. "For some reason, there were scarcely any people on the streets today, and very few came into the barber shop. Finally the owner said I could leave because I wouldn't have any more shoes to shine."

Later in the afternoon Lyndon went to the barn to start doing the evening chores. Rebecca and the other children followed him into the yard to play. "Keep a watchful eye on the younger children, Rebecca," called her mother. "Don't let them do any climbing and don't let them play near the watering trough."

Before long, Sam Johnson came riding home on his horse. He jumped off to let the horse drink at the watering trough. Then he led him into the barn and tied him in his stall. "Thank you, Lyndon, for filling his manger with hay and for pumping water for him to drink. You are a big help to me."

Lyndon, his father, and all the children went to the house for supper. One after another, they took turns dipping water from the rain-barrel and washing at the back of the house. "Sam," called Mrs. Johnson, "I'm so glad you came home to eat with us tonight."

"So am I," asked her husband. "Already I can smell that good boiled beef which you have prepared for supper."

"And I can smell your good cornbread and turnip greens," added Lyndon.

Soon the whole family was seated at the table and Mama asked the blessing. Papa put helpings of food on Sam Houston's plate and Mama on Lucia's plate. All the others at the table served themselves. Everybody ate heartily and there was little conversation.

Finally, when the supper was nearly over, Papa turned to Mama and said, "Rebekah, I have important news for you. I have purchased the newspaper here in Johnson City."

Rebecca pretended to be extremely surprised and Lyndon helped her by remaining quiet. "What?" she exclaimed. "Why in the world did you decide to buy the newspaper?"

"Well, I didn't want to," explained Papa, "but the owner is seriously ill and the doctor has ordered him to move to Arizona. I just couldn't see our town getting along without a newspaper, so I bought it. Now I guess we'll have to do the best we can to run it."

"Will we run the newspaper ourselves?" asked Rebekah. "Will you want me to help?"

There was a moment of silence. "Yes," replied Papa. "You once were a successful teacher. You can handle the English language as well as, or better than, anybody in Johnson City, or all of this Hill Country of Texas. I'll need you to manage the paper and to do most of the editing."

That night when Lyndon went to bed, he was so excited that he could hardly go to sleep. He thought of how strange it would seem to have his mother working downtown. Possibly he could run over to the newspaper office from the barbershop several times a day to see her.

In a few days, Lyndon had an idea. Now that his parents owned the newspaper, he decided to advertise his shoeshine business. He prepared an advertisement and took it over to his mother. "I want to put this ad on the front page of the paper, where people will be sure to see it and to read it," he said.

His mother was amused, but accepted the ad and placed it on the first page, as follows:

Come to the shoeshine stand in Johnson City Barber Shop. Price of shoeshine, 10¢ for shoes. Sunday best, cowboy boots, 20¢. Dirty cattle driving boots, 30¢. Lyndon Johnson, proprietor.

Many persons laughed about the advertisement, but not Lyndon's father. After he came back from a cattle buying trip and caught his first glance of the paper, he cried, "Oh no! I didn't buy a newspaper to advertise that my son is a bootblack." A roar of laughter went up from some of his friends standing nearby. Later two of them slipped over to the barber shop to get their boots shined.

A few weeks later, Lyndon's hound dog, Evelyn, had a litter of nine pups. Shortly thereafter, his father and mother took him into the living room for a talk. "You'll have to get rid of those

SEE ME
FIRST FOR
HOUND PUPS

Lyndon Johnson

pups," said his father. "Soon they'll grow up and it will cost more to feed them than it will to buy food for our family."

Lyndon looked dejected and his mother wiped tears from her eyes. "How can I get rid of them?" he asked, seriously.

"Well, maybe you can sell them, or give them away," replied his father. "Otherwise we may have to drown them."

For several minutes Lyndon sat quietly looking into space. Finally he said, "Let me put up a sign about them in the barbershop."

The next day he prepared the following sign and placed it in front of the barbershop:

See me first for hound pups.

Lyndon B. Johnson

Many people stopped and read his sign. Soon he had new homes for all the pups. He sold all he could, and gave the rest away.

Herding Goats on a Ranch

ONE EVENING about dark Papa lit the kerosene lamp and all members of the family sat down to eat supper. Both parents and children talked and laughed as they ate. Suddenly they were interrupted by loud, screeching sounds coming from the street. "What terrible sounds!" cried Mama. "What's going on?"

Lyndon and his sister, Rebekah, readily recognized the sounds. They had heard them many times at school, and on the way home. Lyndon said nothing, but Rebekah explained, "Some of Lyndon's pals have come to tease him."

"Tease him about what?" asked his mother.

"Because he is taking violin lessons," replied Rebekah. "He happens to be the only boy in town who is taking violin lessons."

"Don't worry about them," said Lyndon. "They're just pretending to imitate me when I practice my lessons on the violin. Before long, they will become tired and go away."

"What are they doing to make such weird sounds?" asked his mother.

Again Rebekah answered. "Well, some of them have gone to great length to tease Lyndon. One of them has made a special noise-making contraption by putting a heavy cord through a hole in the bottom of a tin can. He puts resin on the cord just as a violinist puts resin on the bow of a violin. Then, when he pulls the string back and forth, it makes weird squeaking noises. That's what he and the other boys are doing now out in front of the house."

Lyndon's father was both amused and irritated. He was amused because the sounds from the tin can somewhat resembled the sounds that Lyndon occasionally made when he was practicing. He was irritated because he didn't want anyone to poke fun at a member of his family.

His wife was most irritated. She thought that nobody had a right to tease Lyndon about taking violin lessons. Just as she was about ready to explode, the boys out in front left. Then she changed the subject by bringing out a fresh cream pie. Soon everybody forgot about the teasing episode.

That night after Lyndon went to bed, he rolled around in bed with many thoughts rushing through his head. School would soon be out and he wondered where he could get work for the summer. Maybe he could get a job riding a burro, a pony, or a horse. Every normal boy wanted to ride one of these animals. Some of his friends jokingly referred to his practicing on the violin as riding a violin. "Are you still riding a violin?" they asked, or "Do you wear cowboy boots when you ride the violin?" Finally, he went to sleep hoping that he wouldn't have to ride a violin all summer.

One afternoon soon, as he walked home from school, he noticed a strange man riding a mule, and he could readily tell from the man's appearance that he was a rancher. A few days later, while he was doing the evening chores, the same man rode up to the watering tank near the barn. "Hello there," he said. "May I let my mule get a drink of water?"

"Yes, sir," replied Lyndon. "Let her have all the water she wants."

While the mule drank from the trough, the stranger stood nearby and continued to talk. "You evidently are a school boy," he said. "Will you be happy when your school closes for the summer vacation?"

"Well, I would be if I could get some kind of job," replied Lyndon.

"How fortunate for both of us," exclaimed the stranger. "My goatherd is ill, and I'm looking for someone to take his place for a few months. Can we sit down here by the barn while I ask you a few questions?"

"Sure," answered Lyndon. "Shall I get your mule some hay to eat while we're talking?"

"That would be fine," replied the stranger. "Jennie probably is hungry."

Lyndon quickly brought a forkful of hay and the rancher started to question him. "What is your name?" he asked.

"Lyndon B. Johnson," replied Lyndon. "My father's name is Sam Johnson, Jr."

"I've heard of your father," said the rancher. "He buys livestock around here. Also, I have heard of your grandfather, Sam Ealy Johnson, Sr. Have you ever ridden a mule?"

"No," replied Lyndon, "but I have ridden my father's horse and Dr. Barnwell's burro."

"Well, riding is a skill," commented the rancher. "Some men learn to ride well, and others never do. Do you think you could ride my mule, Jennie?"

"Yes, I think so," replied Lyndon, "but does she have any tricks?"

"Yes, she has a couple of tricks," replied the rancher. "First, if a rider jerks real hard on the bit to slow her down, she'll rear up on her hind legs in an effort to throw him. Second, if a rider accidentally raps the butt of his whip on the horn of her saddle, she may take off right from under him. She has been trained to start moving when this happens, and she really takes off with a vengeance. Would you like to try riding her a short distance, as around the house?"

Lyndon gently rubbed Jennie's forehead and

ears for a minute or two. Then he climbed on her back and calmly rode her about the yard. When he dismounted, the rancher said, "You seemed to know how to handle her, and I think she likes you."

Lyndon's heart was pounding. He felt that he had gained a big step in winning the rancher's confidence. Would he get the job?

"Do you mind being alone by yourself?" asked the rancher. "Some persons never become good herders because they don't like to be alone."

"No," replied Lyndon. "In fact, I like to be alone with such things as rocks, trees, and herds. Somehow they help to keep me company."

"You evidently love nature and that's important," said the rancher. "Now, I'll ask you one more question. Are you afraid of wild animals?"

"No," replied Lyndon. "The largest wild animals in this hilly country are coyotes or wild

dogs, and they seldom attack people or goats during the daytime. Besides, with a sling shot and a large whip like the one you have, I wouldn't be the least bit afraid."

"Good," said the rancher. "I have two trained dogs that accompany my goatherd, so there really is very little danger."

Finally the rancher mounted Jennie and got ready to leave. "I like you, Lyndon," he said. "Talk with your parents about working for me, then I'll telephone your father. Good-by, and thanks for giving Jennie water and hay."

"Good-by," called Lyndon, now feeling as if he lived in a land of make-believe.

That evening before supper Lyndon talked briefly with his father. "Papa must I take violin lessons this summer?" he asked. "I would much rather get a job for the summer." Then he told about talking with the rancher and the possibility of herding goats.

80

"Well, we can't reach a decision about your dropping violin lessons for the summer without having your mother present," said his father. "This evening after supper, you, your mother, and I will have a committee meeting to discuss the matter. Then, if all of us agree that it will be better for you to work this summer, there won't be any problem."

That evening at supper Lyndon's father announced, "Lyndon, your mother and I are going to have a committee meeting after supper. The rest of you may go outdoors to play."

Soon the smaller children left, and Lyndon and his parents remained seated at the table. "The meeting will now come to order," said his father. "Our primary purpose is to decide whether Lyndon shall take violin lessons during the summer. Are there any questions?"

"I should like to inquire why Lyndon wants to quit taking lessons?" asked his mother.

"Lyndon, will you please explain why you wish to discontinue your lessons," said his father.

"The reason is that I want to work during the summer," explained Lyndon. "I already have an opportunity to herd goats this summer." He told about his offer from the goat rancher and explained that the rancher would call to see whether he could take the job.

Lyndon's father and mother looked at each other, as if ready to approve of Lyndon's request. Finally his father said, "Well the question boils down to whether Lyndon will take a job of herding goats. All in favor of him herding goats through the summer say, 'Aye.'"

All three members of the committee voted, "Aye." "The committee has decided by a unanimous vote that Lyndon should take the job of herding goats," said his father. "This decision means that he will be relieved of having to take violin lessons during the summer."

A few days later Lyndon started his work herding goats on the ranch. The rancher gave him his own mule, Jennie, to ride while he worked. At the end of the day, Lyndon proudly rode Jennie back home to Johnson City. Then, the next morning he would ride her back again to the ranch.

When he reached home, he rode Jenny directly to the watering tank near the barn. While she drank, he pulled off her saddle and bridle. Finally he tied her outdoors with a long rope so she could eat grass. All the while he felt very proud, as if he might have grown a foot taller during the day.

That evening, when everybody sat down to eat supper, Lyndon's brothers and sisters had all sorts of questions to ask him about his first day's work. His mother, fearing that the smaller children wouldn't have a chance, asked him to answer their questions first.

"Did Jennie buck you off her back out on the ranch?" asked Sam Houston.

"No," replied Lyndon. "She doesn't buck. She is well trained for herding goats."

"Did you see any wild animals?" asked Lucie, Lyndon's youngest sister.

"Not a one, Lucie," replied Lyndon.

"Not even rattlesnakes?" asked Josefa, his second youngest sister.

"Not a single one," answered Lyndon.

"You must have found it very dull out there all day by yourself with nothing happening," said his oldest sister, Rebekah. "Didn't you see anything exciting during the day?"

"Well, I found it exciting to watch goats climb trees to eat berries," replied Lyndon.

The children looked at him in bewilderment. "Now you're teasing us," said Rebekah. "Goats don't climb trees."

"Not when the trees are standing straight up,"

said Lyndon. "Once today we came to a big tree that had blown down. The goats hopped up on the trunk and climbed out onto the branches to eat twigs and leaves."

"Did any of them fall while they were eating?" asked Sam Houston.

"No," replied Lyndon, "but later when the goats were grazing on a steep hillside, one of the billy goats gave me a big scare. He climbed way out on the trunk of a tree that overhung a small stream. When I first saw him, I could scarcely believe my eyes."

"What happened?" asked Sam Houston. "What did you do to save him?"

"I picked up a small pebble and hit him with my sling shot, but it didn't do any good. He merely bent down as if getting ready to leap. Then, just when I felt sure that he was a goner, he decided to back up."

"I'll bet you felt relieved," said Rebekah.

"Yes, if that billy goat had injured himself, I probably would have lost my job."

"Now let me ask one last question," said his mother. "What do you do with the goats when you come home in the evening?"

"I drive them to a big pen near the ranch house," answered Lyndon. "Then the dogs guard them through the night."

A short time later, his mother said, "It's time to go to bed. You'll have to remember that you are a working man now."

Campaigning with Papa

"I DON'T KNOW whether I'm going to like living here or not," thought Lyndon. "I used to like to come here to see Grandpa and Grandma Johnson, but now it seems strange without them. It really seems like a different place."

Sam Johnson, his wife, and five children had just moved from Johnson City to the farm where his parents had lived. Both Grandpa and Grandma Johnson had died and been buried on the farm, a short distance from the house. It was the custom in the Hill Country of Texas for persons to be buried on their farms.

The house where the Johnsons had moved

was only a quarter of a mile from the cabin in which Lyndon had been born. It was larger and better than any house he ever had lived in before, but he wasn't very happy here.

As a growing boy, he had many chores to do on the farm. He was busy most of the time, but still he felt lonesome. He missed seeing his former friends in Johnson City. He missed shining shoes and listening to interesting conversations in the barbershop.

Every day men gathered at the barbershop in Johnson City to discuss World War I, which now was in progress in Europe. Many bitterly hated Germany for having started the war. They felt that we should clamp down on German-Americans, or persons who had come here from Germany, or whose ancestors had come here from Germany, lest they try to drag our country into the war. Some even argued that we should quit teaching German in our schools.

Early in 1918, shortly after the family had moved to the farm, Sam Johnson was elected to fill an unexpired term as representative to the Texas State Legislature in Austin. Soon after his election, he attended a special session of the legislature, where he helped to pass several important laws. Then during the coming summer and fall, he campaigned to be elected to a full term as representative.

Lyndon was very excited about his father's campaign and liked to accompany him on his trips. Early one morning in July, his father called, "Hurry to get up if you want to go on the campaign trail with me today. We'll need to do the chores before we start."

Immediately Lyndon jumped out of bed and hurried to the barn to join his father. Together they milked the cows and fed and watered all the farm animals. Then they returned to the house where Lyndon's mother had a big breakfast of smoked ham, fried eggs, and biscuits and gravy awaiting them on the table.

While Lyndon and his father were busy eating, his mother sat down to talk with them. "It's a shame that you have to campaign like this in order to be re-elected," she said. "Surely after the active part you played in the last session of the legislature, everybody knows where you stand on the various issues."

"Yes, but times and conditions are changing rapidly," replied her husband. "Remember that our country is engaged in a terrible world war, with young men being drafted by the thousands and sent to Europe, many of whom will never return. This war has brought widespread turmoil in everyday living. Voters are restless and I must get around to talk with them."

"I know, but some people are very unreasonable," said Lyndon's mother. "Ever since Germany started the war in Europe, and even before we entered the war, many people here became prejudiced against German-Americans. Somehow they felt that persons with German backgrounds were disloyal and might betray us. You deserve credit for helping to kill a bill in the last legislature that would have been very unfair to such people."

"Yes, that bill would have made it possible to accuse anybody with a German name of being disloyal," said her husband.

"I don't understand," interrupted Lyndon. "Some of my best friends in Johnson City have German parents and grandparents, and I have never heard them say anything disloyal."

"That's right," said his father, "but as your mother says, ever since Germany started the war in Europe, some of our citizens have come to hate German-Americans. At the same time many German-Americans are respectable, loyal Americans. Many of them live right here in the

Hill Country of Texas. I'm surely glad that I took a stand to protect them."

"Yes, you may be very proud of your father's stand on that issue," said Lyndon's mother. "He made a fine speech about it in the last legislature, which was reported in newspapers all over the state. I'm sure that his speech helped to kill that dreadful bill."

At this point the family political discussion was interrupted by the loud *clang! clang! clang!* of a wall clock, striking the hour of day. "Oh my!" exclaimed Lyndon's father, jumping up from the table. "We must get dressed and take off as soon as possible."

"Must I dress up, too?" asked Lyndon.

"Certainly," replied his father. "You must wear your best Sunday clothes. Put on a clean shirt, clean pants and stockings, and brush your shoes to make them shine. Since it's hot, you may leave off your tie."

Soon Lyndon appeared, dressed just as his father had ordered. He looked admiringly at his father, who was wearing a white shirt with a high collar and a neatly fastened tie. On his head he wore a stiff Stetson hat, which made him look very important.

Lyndon's father owned a model-T Ford. He was one of the few men in the Hill Country to own an automobile. Already he had driven the Model T close beside the house. When he was ready to leave, he cranked the engine, jumped into the front seat, and motioned for Lyndon to join him. Then, waving goodbye to Lyndon's mother, they pulled out onto the dusty road.

Sam Johnson was to make a speech at a picnic dinner at Blanco, about thirty miles away. He planned to stop at Johnson City for a short while. There he would visit the courthouse to talk with county officials and afterwards stand outside in the yard to shake hands with people who happened to come by. Lyndon was happy about stopping and hoped to see some of his friends at the barbershop.

When they reached Johnson City, Lyndon's father went at once to the courthouse. Lyndon headed for the barbershop where he found the barber cutting a customer's hair. "Hello there, Lyndon," the barber cried.

"Hello," Lyndon called back. "My father and I are on the road to Blanco, where he is going to make a speech."

"Yes, I know," said the barber, pausing briefly to talk with Lyndon. "Many people from Johnson City are going over to hear him. They like to hear him speak because he lets them know where he stands on different issues. I wish I could go to hear him, but you may tell him that I plan to vote for him anyhow."

"Thank you, sir," said Lyndon. "I'll be sure to tell him what you said."

Lyndon looked over sorrowfully at the shoe-shine stand where he had worked. The barber noticed the sad expression on his face and said, "if you ever move back here, I want you to work for me again. I wouldn't be surprised that some-day after you grow up, you'll become a repre-sentative in the legislature, just as your father is now. Or you may become a United States Sena-tor, as your grandfather predicted."

Lyndon laughed and held out his hand. "Thank you, sir," he said. "I must go now."

"Good-by, Lyndon," called the barber. "Come back to see me whenever you can."

After Lyndon and his father started on in the Model-T Ford, Lyndon told his father about his trip to the barbershop. "The barber is going to vote for you. He said that people like to hear you speak because you let them know where you stand on different issues. Just what do you mean by an issue?"

"Perhaps I can explain best by giving you an example," replied his father. "One issue which will arise in the next legislature will be the question, 'Shall the University of Texas be required to stop teaching German?' If elected, I'll vote against such a bill. Another issue will be the question, 'Shall the State of Texas buy textbooks for all children attending the public schools?' If elected, I'll vote in favor of such a bill."

"Just what do you want me to do after we reach Blanco?" asked Lyndon.

"Well, at first you can walk around with me and let me introduce you as my son," replied his father. "Then you can saunter around by yourself to visit with people."

"What shall I talk about while I visit with them?" asked Lyndon.

"Really, not much of anything," replied his father. "Just be polite and answer questions. Mostly just listen to what they say about dif-

ferent issues. Then on the way home you can tell me some of the things they say."

In a few minutes Lyndon's father drove into a grove of live oaks. People could be seen sitting at picnic tables in all directions.

"Holy smokes!" cried Lyndon. "Just look!"

97

"Yes, there are far more people here than I expected," replied his father.

After he parked the car, he started to walk about with Lyndon to chat with one family group after another. The people greeted him happily and seemed to be proud to talk with him. Many told him that they planned to vote for him in the election.

Nearly every family group invited him and Lyndon to sit down and eat. Finally they accepted an invitation to join one of the most important political families around Blanco. There was twice as much food as the group could eat, including many different kinds of meat, salads, vegetables, cakes, and pies.

The first thing after dinner was Representative Johnson's talk. Lyndon listened closely as his father discussed one issue after another and told exactly how he would vote on them. The audience often clapped when he finished speaking about an issue. Everybody realized that he was frank and honest, whether they agreed with him or not.

Lyndon listened proudly and thought, "Someday I may be campaigning like this myself."

The campaign continued through the summer into fall. During this period Lyndon's father spoke at dozens of picnics, family reunions, church suppers, ice cream socials, county fairs, and other places where people met in groups. Lyndon went with him constantly, except after school started in the fall.

Finally election day came, and when the voters were counted, Sam Johnson was re-elected representative to the Texas State Legislature for his fourth consecutive term. "We won!" shouted Lyndon, feeling that he had played an important part in the campaign.

"Yes, thanks for your help," said his father.

Straw Boss
and Trapper

ONE EVENING in January while the Johnson family was eating supper, Papa announced to the children, "Come to the living room as soon as you finish eating. Mama and I want to discuss an important family affair with you."

The children looked at one another curiously. They wondered whether their father was going to lay down some new family rules, or whether he was going to scold them for breaking certain rules. Each child finished eating quickly and waited to find out what would happen.

After supper all the children meekly went into the living room followed by Mama and Papa.

"Tomorrow the State Legislature will meet in Austin, and I'll have to be away from home for several weeks," said Papa. "I can't drive so far every day and the weather may be bad much of the time. Besides the legislature will have many night meetings."

"Why does the legislature always meet in the winter?" asked Rebekah.

"One reason is because farmers can get away from home easier during the winter than during the summer. In summer they are very busy cultivating and harvesting crops."

"Yes, but farmers have chores to do in winter," interrupted Lyndon. "They have to look after their horses, cows, sheep, hogs, and poultry every morning and evening."

"That's right, Lyndon," said his father, "and I have called this meeting just to talk about chores. All of you children will have to be responsible for doing some of the chores while I am gone. Each of you will have certain things to do, and I want you to do them without complaining, or shirking. Lyndon, since you are the oldest, you will act as straw boss."

"What particular chores do you want me to do?" asked Lyndon.

"Mostly I want you to work on the wood pile," replied his father. "You can split and carry wood to keep the fires burning. The other children are too young to use the ax."

"May I do the milking?" asked Sam Houston.

"You'll have to ask Lyndon," replied his father. "He will make all the assignments."

Sam Houston looked at Lyndon inquiringly. "Yes, you may do the milking, but you'll also have to feed and water the cows both morning and evening," said Lyndon.

"What shall I do?" asked Rebekah.

"You and Lucia may look after the chickens both morning and evening," replied Lyndon.

102

"Oh good," cried Lucia. "I want to help gather the eggs in the evening."

"Well, just remember that you have to handle eggs very carefully," said Lyndon. "Let Rebekah help you handle them."

"What do you want me to do?" asked Josefa.

"You can carry water for Mama to use in the kitchen," replied Lyndon. "Keep the tank in the stove filled with water for cooking, and bring some additional water for drinking."

The discussion went on until all the chores were assigned. Some children had two or three kinds of chores to do. The older children had much more to do than the younger children. Lyndon decided that he himself would take care of the horses and hogs.

Papa looked proudly at the children. "Now that everything is settled," he said, "I'll bid each of you goodnight. I'll probably leave in the morning before any of you are up."

The children waited in line to bid their father goodnight. When Lyndon, who was last in line, reached his father, he said, "I wish that I could go to Austin with you, Papa. I would like to hear you make speeches and see how you help to pass laws."

"I wish you could, too," said his father, "but right now you have to go to school. Anyhow, just remember that you helped me campaign to get elected again. Now you're helping me by acting as straw boss, so I can take my place in the legislature."

The chore assignments failed to work out as well as Lyndon's father had hoped. During the coming weeks there were many arguments among the children. Some complained that they had more and harder things to do than the others. Lyndon tried hard to settle these arguments, but wasn't always successful.

Later that winter Mama's mother, Grandma

Baines, came to live with the Johnsons. She constantly kept after the children to get them to do their chores. She even criticized Lyndon for not keeping the wood box filled.

Even though Lyndon was busy attending school and acting as family straw boss, he decided to try trapping wild animals on the side. He realized that winter was the best time for trapping because many wild animals, such as rabbits, groundhogs, raccoons, and often foxes, prowled about looking for food. By trapping these wild animals, he hoped to make money by selling pelts and hides and also to bring a few animals home for his mother to cook.

One day he set a string of steel traps and box-like wooden traps in the nearby woods and along the banks of the Pedernales River. The next morning he arose about daylight and took off on horseback to find out what, if any, animals he had caught. He carried a rifle tucked conveniently under his right arm so that he might pick off any animal that he happened to see roaming about.

At first, when he began to examine his traps, he was greatly disappointed. He found the first four steel traps undisturbed, just as he had set them the day before. "Possibly trapping will be poor this winter," he thought. "Maybe most of the animals have left the Hill Country for some area where they can find more to eat. We had a very dry summer season and food is much scarcer than usual."

Soon he came to the fifth steel trap, which he had set near a hollow stump. When he approached the trap, he noticed that the leaves nearby had been disturbed. Loading his rifle, he cautiously approached the stump, ready to shoot, if an animal came dashing out.

When he reached the trap, he found that the jaws had been sprung. He unloaded his rifle and picked up the trap to examine it closely. At once he found some fox hairs on the jaws, which told him that a fox had been caught in the trap. Obviously it had been able to jerk or pull itself loose, because the trap had not been strong enough to hold it. Now there was nothing to do but to reset the trap and to partially conceal it again with leaves.

Soon Lyndon tied his horse to a big tree close by a thicket where he had placed several wooden box traps. He picked up his rifle and walked along an animal trail that led through the dense undergrowth. He found the doors to the first two traps open, which meant that no animals had tried to enter them. "Surely there are animals here somewhere," he thought.

When he reached the third box trap, his heart pounded with excitement. He found the door shut and knew there was an animal inside. Now he must try to find out what the animal was

before he opened the door. He realized that a frightened animal could readily injure him, if he pulled it out without knowing what it was.

He peeked through some holes in the trap and discovered that there was a rabbit inside. Quickly he pulled it out and killed it. Then proudly he put it into an old flour sack to take home to his mother.

As he went on in the thicket, he came to another trap that had a rabbit inside. "Now Mama should be very happy," he said to himself. "With two rabbits she can cook a big meal for the family."

Finally he jumped on his horse and rode to the Pedernales River, where he had set three larger steel traps under water along one of the banks. He found the first two traps empty, but he let out a shout of joy as he glanced in the direction of the third trap. There he beheld the foot of a raccoon projecting from the water.

Evidently the raccoon had been caught in the trap and had drowned.

Joyfully Lyndon put the dead raccoon into another flour sack and tossed it over the back of the horse. When he arrived home, his brothers and sisters rushed out to greet him. "What did you catch?" they asked.

Proudly Lyndon tossed the two flour sacks on the ground. "I caught both meat for the table and a fur to sell," he replied.

"Good," cried Sam Houston. "I'll surely be glad when I can start trapping."

Visiting
the Legislature

DURING THE HOLIDAY season leading up to New Year's Day, 1921, Lyndon was bursting with excitement. His father had promised to take him along to Austin for the next session of the Texas Legislature. Now he would get to hear his father and others make speeches and he would get to watch them vote to pass laws. He felt that making this trip would be the most important thing that he had ever done.

At last the scheduled day came, and Lyndon and his father took off in the family automobile. When they reached Austin, Lyndon was fascinated with the width of Congress Avenue, which led to the capitol building. His father explained that this was one of the widest streets in the state. "Well, it really surprises me," said Lyndon. "Why, it's so wide that people could drive a herd of cattle right down the center of town."

He stared with pride as he caught his first glimpse of the huge capitol building, made of pink granite. He already knew much about this building, even though he had never seen it before. Often his mother had told him how her father, Joseph Baines, who no longer was living, had laid the cornerstone of the building. Grandpa Baines once had held a prominent position in the state government.

When Lyndon and his father entered the building, they chatted with different members of the legislature. His father proudly introduced Lyndon by saying, "This is my oldest son, Lyndon. He helped me to hit the campaign trail in my district and now he wants to see how we make the laws for the state."

During one of Lyndon's first days in Austin, he sauntered along the hallways of the capitol building to look at pictures and paintings hanging on the walls. Soon he came to a painting of General Sam Houston, whom everybody honored as the saviour of Texas. As he stood before the painting, he thought of how Texas once had belonged to Mexico.

In 1836 Sam Houston, with a small army of Texans, had defeated a larger Mexican Army under Santa Anna at San Jacinto to win Texan independence. Then he had served two terms as President of the Republic of Texas. Finally, when Texas had decided to become a state, the people had elected him Senator to represent Texas in the United State Congress.

Lyndon had a special reason for being interested in Sam Houston. His mother had told him that her grandfather once had been minister at a Baptist Church to which Sam Houston belonged. One of her most treasured possessions was a letter which Sam Houston had written to her grandfather. Her great respect for this famous leader helped to explain why she had named Lyndon's brother after him.

As Lyndon walked on down the hall, he felt very proud to be the son of a Texas legislator, and the grandson of the man who had laid the cornerstone of the state capitol building. He now was only thirteen and one-half years old, but he looked forward to the time when he, too, could serve his state in some way. He felt eager to uphold the records which his father and his grandfather had established.

That afternoon he went with his father to the hall where the representatives met. His father always went early to meetings so he could discuss important issues with other representatives.

He wanted to find out whether they planned to vote for or against these issues. He probably knew more about how members would vote than any other member of the legislature.

Sam Johnson shared a desk in the legislature with another representative, named Wright Patman. There was merely room enough for these two men to sit comfortably. Lyndon's father tried to slide over enough to make room for Lyndon at one end of the seat. There was so little room, however, that Lyndon spent much of his time standing. All the while he watched and listened to learn all that he could.

At this time the Ku Klux Klan was very active in Texas. This was an organization in which the members wore white sheets about their bodies and white pillow-cases over their heads so people couldn't tell who they were. Often they took the law in their own hands and carried on acts to frighten and terrorize people.

Representative Patman was strongly opposed to the Ku Klux Klan. One day he said to Lyndon's father, "Let's introduce a bill in the legislature to control this organization. We can't accomplish anything just by opposing it. We must take positive action."

"I agree," said Lyndon's father, pounding his fist on the top of their desk. "Let's spring a surprise attack on them, just as Sam Houston did on Santa Anna."

"What do you suggest?" asked Representative Patman.

"I suggest that we introduce a bill to keep them from hiding behind sheets and pillowcases while threatening people," said Lyndon's father. "Maybe if they have to come right out in the open and show who they are, they won't stir up so much trouble."

"That's right," said Representative Patman. "I'll introduce a bill to make it a penitentiary offense for anyone to wear a disguise with the intent of harming others."

"Good," snapped Lyndon's father. "I will co-sponsor your bill. You start to prepare it and I'll begin to sound out representatives to see

how they feel about it. Then I'll prepare three lists of names. The first list will include the names of representatives whom we know will vote for our bill. The second list will include the names of representatives whom we know will vote against it. The third list will include the names of representatives whom we're not certain about. Then I'll work on the persons on the third list, to get as many additional votes as possible."

Representative Patman sat down at his desk and started to write the bill. Lyndon's father went into the hallway to start convincing other representatives that it was needed. Both were determined to put on a strong campaign to have the bill passed.

Lyndon watched closely as his father talked with one of the representatives about the bill. He stood face to face with him and looked him straight in the eyes. He repeatedly jerked the lapels of his coat to emphasize what he was saying. Soon the representative began to nod his head to show that he agreed with him.

Before long, Patman came down the hallway and noticed Lyndon's father talking with this representative. "Sam Johnson has a cowboy style all his own," he thought. "He thinks clearly, fights hard, and goes straight to the heart of things. His son, Lyndon, who is almost a carbon copy of him, is sure to succeed."

Each week-end Lyndon and his father drove back to their home in the Hill Country of Texas. They always were happy when they descended into the little valley where they lived. The legislature was exciting, but there was nothing like being at home with the persons they loved.

A Cotton-Picking Party

SAM JOHNSON and his brother, Tom Johnson, raised cotton together. The cotton field was on Tom Johnson's farm, which was next to Sam Johnson's farm. Often Lyndon worked in the cotton field with his father and Uncle Tom. At last big bolls broke open on the cotton plants, and the cotton was ready to pick.

Cotton pickers were hard to find, because most farm workers had steady jobs. At last, Sam Johnson and his brother Tom decided to hold a cotton picking party. They would invite older boys and girls from Johnson City to help with picking cotton. Then they would serve them a big fried chicken dinner at noon, and ice cream and cake at the end of the day.

One day Lyndon rode into Johnson City with Uncle Tom to invite boys and girls to come to the party. The first person he met was one of his cousins, Truman Fossett. "Truman," he shouted, "how would you like to come to a cotton picking party at our place in the morning? You'll get a big chicken dinner at noon and ice cream and cake in the evening."

"That sounds wonderful," answered Truman. "You may count on me as one of your pickers. Who else will be there?"

"Most of the older boys and girls here in Johnson City, I hope," replied Lyndon. "I'll appreciate your helping me to invite as many as possible. Tell them to come to the courthouse at six o'clock in the morning for a wagon ride out to the farm. The only requirements are to have strong backs and big appetites."

Lyndon and Truman went here and there to invite their friends to the party. Soon most of the boys and girls in town knew about it and planned to attend. They looked forward to the fun of talking and laughing as they worked together out in the big cotton field. Also, they looked forward to gorging themselves on fried chicken, ice cream, and cake.

Promptly at six o'clock the next morning Uncle Tom picked up a wagon load of boys and girls at the courthouse. He drove them directly to the packing shed at one end of the big cotton field. There he and his son, Ealy, who was about Lyndon's age, passed out long picking sacks to the pickers.

Some of the boys and girls had trouble getting the straps on their picking sacks over their heads. "The strap on my sack is too short," said a boy. "I can't get it over my head."

"The strap is all right," said one of the girls

teasingly. "The trouble is the size of your head." Everybody laughed.

Another boy, dancing about foolishly, tripped on his sack and fell flat on his face. "What a clumsy act," said one of the girls. "Boys certainly are more clumsy than girls."

"Boys may be more clumsy than girls, but they can pick more cotton than girls," retorted one of the boys.

"You're just bragging," said a girl. "We girls are ready to show you boys that we can pick just as much cotton as you can."

Suddenly Tom Johnson called out, "Attention, boys and girls. Some of you are arguing whether boys can pick more cotton than girls. Suppose we have a contest today to settle that question. We'll weigh and make a record of all the cotton that the boys pick, and of all the cotton that the girls pick.

"The winners in the contest, whether boys or

girls, will be served first at the ice cream party this evening. Also, they may have an extra dish of ice cream apiece and choose the kind of cake they want."

"We'll win," shouted several boys, eager to get started.

"Now everybody listen while I give you a few instructions on picking," called Sam Johnson. "The boys will start picking on the west side of the field, and the girls on the east side. When a picker reaches the end of a row, he will start back on another unpicked row. One boy may help another finish a row and one girl may help another finish a row. Pick only the bolls that are ripe. Be careful not to put stems and leaves in your sacks."

The boys lined up at the ends of rows on the west side of the field and the girls at the ends of rows on the east side of the field. Moments later, Tom Johnson shouted, "Get set, go!"

Quickly the pickers started down along their rows, picking ripe cotton and poking it into their long sacks. Soon they discovered that their sacks became harder and harder to drag. Every so often each picker had to drag his sack of cotton to the packing shed to have the cotton removed and weighed.

Late in the forenoon the children became hot, exhausted, and hungry. They kept waiting for the time to eat and to rest. One boy said, "Won't noon ever come today? I never have been so tired in my life. I'm so hungry I could eat a whole chicken by myself."

At noon, when Tom Johnson banged the bottom of a big pan to call the children to dinner, they dropped their long picking sacks right where they were. After they congregated, he announced that the boys and girls were about equal in the number of pounds of cotton they had picked. Then he led them to a nearby picnic table which was loaded with fried chicken, baked ham, baked beans, sweet corn, green vegetables, and all sorts of jellies and jams.

Tom Johnson's wife, Kittie, was there to greet the children. She invited them to take plates and help themselves to the food. At once they swarmed about the table and stacked their plates high with food. They decided that Kittie Johnson was a mighty fine cook.

After dinner, the girls helped Mrs. Johnson clear away the dishes and left-over food. They put the dishes in big tubs, ready to be washed, and carried the left-over food into the kitchen. Then they stretched out on beds and floors for a short rest.

While the girls rested inside the yard, the boys stretched out in the shade of a large tree. As they talked, Lyndon tried to think of something exciting to do. "How many of you have ever tried to ride a steer?" he asked.

126

Some of the boys had tried to ride a steer and some hadn't. "How in the world can you get on a steer?" asked one of the boys.

"Oh that's easy," explained Lyndon. "Usually you have some friends herd him into the corner of a pen, so you can climb on. Then they turn him loose with you on his back."

"How can you guide him without a bridle or halter?" asked another boy.

"You can't," replied Lyndon. "That's part of the fun of it. You have to guess which way he will go by the way he turns his head. He'll try to outsmart you to throw you off."

"Yes, and in many cases, he succeeds," added Lyndon's cousin, Ealy.

Lyndon and Ealy offered to take the boys to a feedlot, where they could try riding some steers. "We can have fun while the girls are still resting in the house," they said.

When they reached the feedlot, Lyndon offered to ride a steer first, so the others could see what they would have to do.

Ealy and a few other boys crowded one of the steers into a corner and Lyndon slid on his back from a nearby fence. He grabbed the hair on the steer's neck, just in front of his shoulders, and called, "Now let him go."

The steer lurched forward, but suddenly turned to the right. Lyndon leaned to the right, and his body slid to the left. When his left foot hit the ground, he shoved himself right back upon the steer. Next the steer suddenly turned to the left. Lyndon leaned to the left, and his body slid to the right. When his right foot hit the ground, he shoved himself back up on the steer again. Finally, the steer ran straight ahead a few yards and stopped suddenly, with his head down. Lyndon, caught by surprise, slid over the steer's head and landed standing upright directly in front of him.

By now Lyndon had made riding a steer look so easy that all the boys wanted to try riding one. One boy after another mounted a steer and soon found himself sitting or sprawling on the ground. Not one could stay on very long.

The steers played all kinds of tricks. They lurched to the right, or left, to throw the boys off sideways. They ran forward and stopped suddenly to throw the boys over their heads. They jumped right out from under some of the boys, causing them to come plump down in a sitting position on the ground. They ran close to the wooden fence to brush the boys off.

Finally the boys gave up, but some of them had different sorts of injuries. One had a cut in his nose, and another had a swelling on his forehead. Many had scratched or skinned elbows and knees. All seemed to be proud to point out what had happened to them.

In the excitement they had completely forgotten about picking cotton. Lyndon looked up at the sun to estimate the time and noted that it was near the middle of the afternoon. "We must hurry back to the cotton field," he cried. "Already we're an hour or so late. The girls are way ahead of us."

The boys were in no mood for hurrying back

130

to the cotton field. Some were so banged and scratched up that they didn't want to go back at all. At last, however, all of them returned and picked the best they could.

At the end of the day, everybody knew which side had won the cotton-picking contest. The boys had lost out by playing hooky part of the afternoon. Likewise everybody knew who had won the steer riding contest. All the boys, except Lyndon, knew from their bruises and scratches that the steers had won.

Visiting the Alamo

LYNDON WAS in the haymow on the second floor of the big barn on the farm. He was spreading forkfuls of freshly-cut hay, which his father pitched up to him from the hayrack on a wagon. The afternoon sun shone directly on the roof of the barn, and the temperature in the haymow was over 100° Fahrenheit.

Finally Lyndon's father pitched up the last forkful of hay from the hayrack, and Lyndon climbed down a ladder from the haymow. Both he and his father were hot, sweaty, thirsty, and tired from pitching hay in such hot weather. They shook and brushed themselves to get rid of particles of hay and dust which were clinging to their clothing and skin.

Outside the barn they went directly to the well to cool off. First, they filled a couple of buckets of water which they used to wash the sweat and dust from their faces, arms, and hands. Then they filled a couple of gourds with water to quench their thirst.

As they stood drinking, Lyndon's father said, "There's only one more load of hay in the field. I think we'll bring it in today so we'll have tomorrow free."

"Are you planning to go somewhere tomorrow?" asked Lyndon.

"Possibly," replied his father. "A man from San Antonio is supposed to telephone me tonight, and I may need to make a trip there tomorrow. Once when we were campaigning nearby I remember that you wanted to go there."

"Yes, but you were too busy making speeches

to take me," said Lyndon. "I've always wanted to see the Alamo in San Antonio."

"Well, this may come as a surprise," said his father, "but if I have to go to San Antonio tomorrow, you may go with me."

"Oh good," cried Lyndon. "By all means I want to go with you."

"I was sure you would, but right now we must go after that last load of hay," said his father. "I'll go to the house to tell your mother that we may be a little late for supper. Also, I'll ask her to have Sam Houston, Rebekah, and her sisters do the chores this evening. Then we won't have to do them when we finish putting the hay in the haymow."

The rest of the afternoon passed quickly and quietly. Lyndon and his father brought the last load of hay and put it in the haymow. That evening while they were washing for supper, Lyndon's father received his expected telephone call. Moments later, he returned and said, "Well, son, we're going to San Antonio. At last you'll get to see the Alamo."

Lyndon never had been happier in his life. He could scarcely believe that the next day he would take such a wonderful trip. That night when he went to bed he was too excited to sleep. Instead he tried to recall the many interesting things which he had learned about San Antonio and the Alamo in school.

In 1835, San Antonio was a small city of about 2,500 people. Inside the city was a small Spanish mission, or church, called San Antonio de Valero. This mission had been built by early Spanish settlers and explorers. Later it had been taken over by Spanish and Mexican military forces and used for stationing troops. Also, its name had been changed to Alamo, because it was surrounded by cottonwood trees. Alamo is the Spanish word for cottonwood.

135

In December, 1835, Bexar County, in which San Antonio is located, was in the control of Mexican military forces. A Texan rifleman, named Ol' Ben Milan, organized a small band of Texan volunteers to attempt to seize Bexar County from the Mexicans. Standing in the stirrups astride his favorite horse, he shouted to his men, "Who'll go into Bexar County with Ol' Ben Milan?"

"We will," replied his troops. "Ride on."

Ol' Ben wheeled his horse and rode into Bexar County accompanied by these brave volunteers. They captured San Antonio and the Alamo, but Ol' Ben Milan was killed. His death made the volunteers fight all the harder.

The remaining 187 volunteers now took over the Alamo and used it as their headquarters. People all over Texas admired them for their courage but feared for their safety. Soon a big Mexican army crossed the Rio Grande and headed for San Antonio, determined to massacre the small group of defenders. In February, 1836, it laid siege to the Alamo and a few weeks later killed every single man.

Finally, after recalling this dreadful story, Lyndon managed to fall asleep. The next morning he was so exhausted from harvesting hay the previous day that he failed to awaken until he heard someone calling him. "Come, Lyndon," shouted his father. "You'll have to get up immediately if you want to go to Bexar County and San Antonio with me today."

When Lyndon heard the words, "Bexar County" and "San Antonio," he awakened instantly. "I'm coming, Papa," he called in reply.

Right after breakfast Lyndon climbed into the automobile with his father for the drive to San Antonio. Along the way he talked almost constantly about Texas history. "Can we drive on to Goliad on this trip?" he asked.

"I'm afraid not," replied his father, "but why do you want to go there?"

"Because that's where another terrible massacre took place," replied Lyndon. "At Goliad the Mexican soldiers killed Colonel James W. Fannin and his men in cold blood. Later, when General Sam Houston won independence for Texas at the Battle of San Jacinto, his soldiers went into battle crying, 'Remember the Alamo! Remember Goliad!' "

"Yes, there were massacres at both the Alamo and Goliad, but unfortunately there is nothing to see at Goliad," said his father. "Everything there has been destroyed."

"Well, I'm certainly glad there still is something to see at the Alamo," said Lyndon. "Didn't you help to get the Texas legislature to take action to purchase it?"

"Yes," replied his father. "During one session of the legislature I was appointed to a committee

138

on public lands. Our committee introduced a bill called the Alamo Purchase Act, authorizing the governor to purchase the Alamo and surrounding land. Now the old mission is preserved as a historical site."

A little later Lyndon said, "I read in history that the old Chisholm Trail once led from San Antonio northeast into Kansas. Did Grandpa Johnson ever drive cattle from San Antonio over the Chisholm Trail to Kansas?"

"I really don't know," replied his father. "It seems reasonable to guess, however, that he drove cattle eastward from the Hill Country to the Chisholm Trail and then followed it northward on into Kansas. This trail swung around to the east of the Hill Country where the land was fairly level."

By this time Lyndon and his father had left the Hill Country and entered a level region which continued southward to San Antonio.

This region was very different from the Hill Country. There were fewer trees and the farms looked more prosperous, with darker soil and better crops. The pastures looked better, with more grass for animals to eat.

When Lyndon and his father reached San Antonio, his father dropped him off at the Alamo while he went on to look after business. Excitedly Lyndon walked across the courtyard and entered the old chapel. Inside he found many posters and maps on the walls which helped him to recall the details of the massacre.

In February, 1836, while the Texas volunteers were occupying the Alamo, General Antonio Lopez de Santa Anna had crossed the Rio Grande into Texas with an army of about 4,000 Mexican soldiers. On February 23, he had reached San Antonio and laid siege to the Alamo. From then on, the volunteers on the inside had been unable to obtain food and water.

The 187 Texas volunteers inside the Alamo had put up a gallant fight. Their number had included such prominent heroes as James Bowie, William B. Travis, and Davy Crockett. For twelve days they had managed to hold off the larger Mexican army. Finally in March, the Mexican cannon had broken a hole in the mission wall and the Mexican soldiers had stormed in and slaughtered all the gallant defenders. In the meantime the defenders had killed over one thousand Mexican soldiers.

After Lyndon finished looking about inside the chapel, he returned to the courtyard. Soon he heard his father calling from the street, "Lyndon, are you ready to go home?"

"Yes, Papa," he answered sorrowfully. Somehow he felt that in visiting the Alamo, he had been walking on hallowed ground.

High School and Afterwards

IN THE SPRING of 1920, when Lyndon was eleven years old, he graduated from a one-room school, which included only seven grades. The following spring he graduated from the eighth grade of an elementary school in the village of Stonewall. That fall, when he was thirteen, he arranged to attend a three-year high school in the village of Albert.

This high school was about four miles from the Johnson home, so Lyndon planned to ride horseback to and from the village each day. "Won't you get tired of riding so far all alone?" asked his mother one evening at supper. "You'll have to ride about eight miles every day to and from school."

"Oh, no," replied Lyndon. "I'll enjoy riding through the country in the morning and late afternoon. There'll be many interesting things to see and do along the way."

On his way to high school, he crossed the Pedernales River and turned southward to Albert. At first he found his trips exciting because everything was strange to him. Then gradually he became acquainted with some of the people along the way and enjoyed talking with them. Often in the late afternoon they invited him to stop for something to eat.

In high school Lyndon had trouble keeping busy. He learned his lessons readily and was eager to do extra reading, but he could find few suitable books in the school library. His chief recreation was playing baseball with the other boys at recess and noon.

One recess after he finished playing baseball he sat down under a shade tree to rest. A high school girl sat nearby, but neither spoke to each other. Suddenly, Lyndon broke the silence by saying, "Someday I am going to be President of the United States."

"Gosh!" exclaimed the girl. She was so surprised that this was all she could say.

During Lyndon's second year in high school, his father suffered serious financial problems. There was little money with which to buy food and clothing for the children and feed for the farm animals. Even the horse which Lyndon rode to school began to show his ribs.

Lyndon was worried but said nothing. From some of his parents' remarks, he concluded that they were planning to move back to Johnson City. Finally one evening at the supper table, his mother suddenly asked, "How would you children like to live in Johnson City again?"

All the children, except Lyndon, looked wide-eyed at one another in surprise. Only Lyndon, Rebekah, and Sam Houston could remember living in Johnson City. Josefa and Lucia had been too young to remember.

"Well, I would like to live there again," said Lyndon. "Then maybe I can get back my old job of shining shoes. If not, I can find other odd jobs, such as washing windows, mowing lawns, or hoeing gardens."

"Can I get a job in Johnson City?" asked Sam Houston.

"Probably," replied his mother. "Lyndon had a job there at your age."

"I think I'll like living there because I'll have a chance to get acquainted with more girls of my age," said Rekebah.

At that moment the children's father spoke up and said, "Well, you all seem to agree that you would like to live in Johnson City again. We'll

146

plan to move there sometime in August before the opening of school."

The high school in Johnson City, like the high school at Albert, contained only three years. Lyndon enrolled as a senior and spent a busy year. He was elected president of the senior class, which included four members beside himself. He was a member of the high school baseball team and the debate team.

In baseball, the team played teams from other high schools in Blanco County. It won several games and had a successful season. Usually Lyndon played either as pitcher or outfielder.

In debate the school took part in a tournament sponsored by the Texas Interscholastic League. The question in 1924 was, "Resolved that the United States withdraw troops from Nicaragua." Lyndon studied this question thoroughly to become fully informed.

The other member of the debate team was a

boy named Johnnie Casparis. Lyndon and Johnnie won all the debates in Blanco County. Next, they entered a large regional contest in which they won third place. Lyndon was greatly disappointed because he had hoped that they could become state champions.

Outside of school Lyndon found many jobs to keep him busy. He got back his shoeshining job in the barber shop, where he worked a few hours every weekday. On Friday and Saturday nights he passed out handbills in the lobby of the movie theatre, which was located over the firehouse. By passing out these handbills, he got to see all the movies free.

When Lyndon graduated from Johnson City High School the following spring, he was over six feet tall but was only fifteen years of age going on sixteen. At the graduation exercises he read the class poem, gave the class prophecy, and delivered the valedictory address. His admiring classmates predicted that sometime he would become governor of Texas.

After the glamour and excitement of graduating from high school wore off, Lyndon faced the problem of making a decision about his future. He had little choice between getting a job and going to college. His father still was too poor to help send him to college.

Soon his father obtained a job for him in Robstown, Texas, but he received such small wages that he could barely live. Before long he resigned and returned home.

Back in Johnson City, he persuaded five friends to join him in going to California to look for work. The six boys pooled their money and bought an old dilapidated Model T Ford. Then they spent more money buying parts to repair the car. Finally, when they were ready to leave, they had spent so much money on the car that they had little left for traveling.

Lyndon's father was bitterly opposed to Lyndon going to California. He thought that Lyndon was too young to take off on such a long trip with a group of boys. For this reason the boys waited for an opportunity to leave while he was away on a business trip.

Their trip was much slower and harder than they had anticipated. All they had to eat were slices of fatback and cornbread with molasses, which they had brought from home. Each night they slept on the ground besides the road. During the latter part of their trip, they ran out of both food and money. Without money they could purchase neither gasoline for their car nor food for their stomachs. They had to stop and work at odd jobs from time to time to earn money before they could go on.

At last they reached southern California, tired, hungry, sunburned, and wind-burned. They had expected to find California a land of

150

golden opportunity with plenty of work, but they were doomed to disappointment. They looked and looked for jobs where they could work together, but finally had to split up in order to find any work at all.

Lyndon was determined to stay on for a while, even though he could find no steady employment. He hitchhiked and tramped up and down the coast, working on farms, cultivating gardens, waiting table, washing dishes, or working at any other jobs he could find. At night, if he was working in the country, he slept outdoors, and if he was working in the city, he slept in a cheap rooming house.

Early in 1926, after staying in California about eighteen months, he decided to return to Johnson City. He had little money, so he hitchhiked all the way. When he reached home, he looked like skin and bones.

Lyndon's parents urged him to stop working

and go to college even though they could do little to help him financially. In reply, he insisted that he still wanted to keep on working for a while.

During the coming months he worked at several low-paying jobs in and around Johnson City. Finally his father, who was a foreman of a road gang, gave him a job which paid a dollar a day. On this job he drove a truck, pushed a wheel-barrow and shoveled gravel and dirt. He had to work outdoors in all kinds of weather, which ranged from scorching hot to penetrating cold. Often he got caught in a skin-soaking rain with no means of protection.

One rain-swept morning in February, 1927, he suddenly dashed into the house and announced, "Mama, if you and Papa can get me in, I'm ready to go to college."

"Oh, good," cried his mother. "We'll certainly do all we can to help you."

Busy Years
at College

ONCE LYNDON had decided to go to college, he was eager to get started. He wanted to make up for lost time and get his degree as soon as possible. He planned to attend school twelve months a year to speed up his work.

He hoped to enroll at Southwest Texas State Teacher's College at San Marcos, but the winter term had already started. His mother telephoned the President, Dr. Cecil Evans, to ask whether he still could get in. Also, she inquired about his expenses, including his tuition, books, board and room, and whether he could work to help pay his way at the college.

Lyndon could hardly wait for his mother to stop talking. As soon as she hung up, he started to ask questions. "What did Dr. Evans say?" he inquired. "May I enroll?"

"Yes, he said for you to come on, that you still may enroll even though classes have started," replied his mother.

"What did he say about my expenses?" asked Lyndon. "How much money will I need?"

"Your tuition and books will be about ten dollars a month and your board and room about a dollar a day," answered his mother.

"Thank you, Mama," he said. "You surely have done me a big favor."

Lyndon figured that he would have to raise about seventy-five dollars to get started. He knew that his parents couldn't let him have the money, so he went to the bank in Johnson City and asked for a loan. The banker refused and Lyndon left stunned and dejected.

When he reached home, his mother tried to console him. At once she telephoned the bank in Blanco, fourteen miles away. "I want to make arrangements for my son, Lyndon, to talk with you," she said.

Lyndon willingly made the trip to Blanco. When he returned, he happily announced, "I have the seventy-five dollars. The banker even let me sign the note all by myself."

That night Lyndon packed his suitcase in order to get an early start to San Marcos the next morning. After breakfast he kissed all the members of the family good-by and went out to the street to hitchhike his way. Soon he picked up a ride and within a few hours arrived at the college.

That same day he conferred with President Evans, enrolled as a student, rented a room, and obtained a job. His first job was to clean up trash from the college campus, but soon he became assistant janitor of the science building. Each evening he pushed a huge brush broom to clean the floors. While working, he prepared his lessons by reciting them out loud.

Within a short time, he decided that since he was in college, he should get a job using his head instead of his hands. One day he dashed into President Evans' office and asked to work for him. The President courteously explained that he had a full-time secretary and didn't need anybody else. Lyndon was so persistent, however, that he finally employed him as assistant secretary to work during his free periods between classes.

Gradually Lyndon became a very helpful assistant. He worked in a room outside the President's office, where he had an opportunity to meet many visitors. Later he began to inquire what various persons wanted and even to suggest means of solving their problems.

President Evans liked Lyndon and admired him for his ability, energy, honesty, and friendly manner. Gradually he turned over more and more paper work to him, such as answering routine letters, filling in forms, and preparing reports. He even took him along on some of his business trips to Austin.

Lyndon was equally successful in working out his program of studies at the university. Since he had only graduated from a three-year high school, he had to make up a year of high school credits. Accordingly he enrolled in the college laboratory school to earn the extra credits which he needed. He was such a brilliant student, however, that he completed the necessary courses in a few months and became a full-fledged college student.

In his regular college work he majored in history and other social sciences. He made such high grades in these courses that he was invited to join the National Social Science Honor Society, Pi Gamma Mu. Also, he took the required courses in education to obtain a permanent, or lifetime, high school teaching certificate in the State of Texas.

In addition to carrying a full load of college courses and working to earn a living, he engaged in many special activities. As a freshman, he wrote a weekly article for the college newspaper, the *College Star*. A year later, he became editor of this newspaper, and the first sophomore, or second-year student, ever to hold this important position. As editor, he not only gained valuable writing experience, but he earned a salary of thirty dollars a month, on which he managed to live.

Early in his college career, he became interested in campus politics. He helped to form a new political group to fight the old political group which had been ruling the campus for

years. This new group soon won the election and dislodged the old group.

Right at the peak of Lyndon's college career, he suffered a serious interruption. His father's financial condition became worse and he had to drop out to help support his family. By now he had earned enough credits to teach in Texas elementary schools. Promptly Dr. Evans helped him to obtain a teaching position in Cotulla, Texas, at a salary of one hundred twenty-five dollars a month.

His class at Cotulla was made up of sixth- and seventh-grade Mexican-Americans. He had to teach these pupils English before he could teach them arithmetic, history, and other subjects. This was a difficult task, but he set a brilliant record.

As a teacher, he took a personal interest in his pupils and did many things on the side to help them. Once he took a failing boy home with him to Johnson City to give him special help, which enabled the boy to pass.

Fortunately, Southwest Texas State Teachers' College offered extension courses at Cotulla, where Lyndon was teaching. He took several courses and was able to add twelve credits to his record. These credits helped to speed up his date for graduation.

In 1929, after his father's financial condition had somewhat improved, he returned to college for the summer. By now he had enough credits so that by attending school continuously, he could graduate in August the following year.

His last year in college was a huge success. He became a member of the debating team and one of the most successful debaters the college ever had. He served as president of the college press club and wrote many articles for publication. He was a member and leader of almost every student organization on the campus.

In August 1930, Lyndon B. Johnson graduated from Southwest Texas Teachers' College with a bachelor of science degree. He was qualified to teach high school in the State of Texas.

A short time later he obtained a position to teach debating and public speaking in the Sam Houston High School in Houston. During that year he coached the high school debate team which won the Houston city championship, and then went on to win the regional state championship. Already he had proved himself to be an able and inspiring teacher.

From Teacher to Vice-President

LYNDON B. JOHNSON started his political career in July, 1930, when he was still twenty-one years old, but soon would be twenty-two. He was still a college student, preparing to graduate in August.

During that summer Pat Neff was running for re-election as governor of Texas. He was opposed by Gregory Hatcher, who was campaigning hard to defeat him. Lyndon's father was eager for Mr. Neff to win, because Mr. Neff had appointed him to a position as state bus inspector. If Mr. Hatcher should win the election, Lyndon's father would lose his job.

In July, 1930, an all-day regional political rally was held in a live-oak grove near Henly, about seventeen miles from Johnson City. Lyndon's father planned to attend the meeting and invited Lyndon to accompany him to help urge people to vote for Mr. Neff. He was proud of Lyndon for his friendly nature and rare ability to persuade people.

Despite the blistering hot weather, several hundred sun-tanned farmers and ranchers attended the rally. There were several candidates present, all of whom spoke from a wagon which was used as a platform. Much of the time while these candidates pleaded for votes, the listeners ate watermelons.

Neither candidate for governor attended the meeting. Gregory Hatcher had arranged for a man to speak for him, but Pat Neff had not. Lyndon's father was worried. "It's poor politics for Pat Neff not to be here or to have somebody to take his place," he said. "I only hope that somebody will speak up for him."

The announcer called for someone to speak for Mr. Hatcher, as candidate for governor. The man whom Mr. Hatcher had sent promptly climbed upon the wagon and explained that he had come to speak for the next governor of Texas. Then all of Mr. Hatcher's supporters shouted and clapped their hands.

The speaker, encouraged by this cheering, decided to lambaste Pat Neff and tear him apart, limb from limb. "Pat Neff is a stuffed shirt," he shouted. "He's a city slicker who doesn't know anything about your problems, and cares less. He has lost touch completely with people who live on the land. Why, he doesn't even go hunting or fishing. He doesn't know whether you hunt or fish for a raccoon."

Again the listeners laughed and cheered, and the speaker started to lambaste Pat Neff all the

166

harder. They interrupted frequently with shouts of approval. By now Lyndon's father was almost frantic with fear. He could see that this speech was going over big with the farmers and ranchers from the Hill Country of Texas.

When the Hatcher man finished speaking, he jumped down from the wagon. All the Hatcher supporters in the audience shouted and clapped with glee. They felt that they had won the day in pulling votes from Pat Neff.

The announcer, out of courtesy, inquired whether anyone would like to speak for Pat Neff. At once Lyndon plunged through the crowd and shouted, "I'll speak for Pat Neff."

Swiftly Lyndon climbed onto the wagon. The announcer looked at him in surprise. Then he turned toward the audience and said simply, "Sam Johnson's boy, Lyndon."

Lyndon wasted no time in getting started. He spoke freely and earnestly, applying the tactics which he had learned as a debater. He used hard-hitting language and gestured freely to emphasize what he said. He chewed to pieces the former speaker's arguments and ridiculed his jokes. For instance, he said, "Maybe Pat Neff doesn't hunt or fish, but what does that matter? Certainly you wouldn't want him to come out here hunting, when he can't tell a deer from a steer. Do you want to take a chance on him shooting your cattle?"

When Lyndon finished speaking, the listeners went wild. They shouted and clapped their hands to let him know how they felt. He had made the best speech of the day and he'd swung the votes back to Pat Neff.

A candidate for the state senate, who was present, was especially pleased with Lyndon's speech. He rushed over to Lyndon and asked him to help manage his campaign. Lyndon accepted and the candidate won the election.

In September, 1931, Lyndon returned to his position as teacher of debating and public speaking in the Sam Houston High School. Soon, however, Richard M. Kleberg, a candidate for Representative in the United States Congress, invited him to help conduct his campaign. Kleberg won the November election and liked Lyndon so well that he invited him to become his private secretary. Lyndon accepted and moved to Washington, D. C., ready to embark on a political career.

As a newcomer, young Lyndon B. Johnson sought to get acquainted as soon as possible with important political leaders in Washington. In later years he often referred to Franklin D. Roosevelt, who became President in 1933, as his "First Daddy" in the national capitol. He referred to a Texan, Sam Rayburn, who was Speaker of the House of Representatives, as his "Second Daddy" in the capitol.

The secretaries to congressmen had an organization, which they called "Little Congress." About a year and a half after Johnson went to Washington, he was elected president of this organization. He was the first person ever to hold this office without working his way up through the other offices.

On one of his trips back to Texas, he happened to meet Claudia Taylor, whom everybody called Lady Bird Taylor. He started to court her, and in a few months, proposed marriage. She accepted and they traveled to Mexico on their honeymoon.

Johnson served as private secretary to Congressman Kleberg for about four years. Finally the congressman's wife asked her husband to fire him because she felt he was making too many decisions.

A month after Lyndon lost his job, President Roosevelt appointed him National Youth Ad-

ministrator for the state of Texas. He accepted and he and Lady Bird moved back to Texas. In the capacity of Youth Administrator for Texas, he made a notable record.

In the spring of 1937, Johnson's father urged him to run for representative to the United States Congress in a special election to fill the place of a representative who had died. At first he hesitated because he had to borrow money with which to conduct his campaign. He readily won the election, however, and returned to Washington. Both his father and mother were very proud of him for becoming a member of Congress. Unfortunately his father died later that same year.

Young Johnson became a very popular representative and later was elected to five full terms from his district. In 1941, with encouragement from President Roosevelt, he decided to become a candidate for United States Senator from

Texas, but he was defeated. This was the only time in his political career that he ever lost an election.

During this exciting period in Johnson's life, World War II had started in Europe. Germany had attacked several nearby countries and later had been joined by Italy in a war of aggression. Other European countries, including England and France, had formed a group, called the Allies, to protect themselves. Our country had taken a position of neutrality and had tried hard to stay out of the conflict.

In time Japan joined the war on the side of Germany and Italy and began to attack countries in and along the Pacific Ocean. Suddenly and unexpectedly on December 7, 1941, Japan attacked Pearl Harbor, one of our military bases in Hawaii. At once we declared war on Japan, and in return Germany and Italy declared war on us. Now we were forced to fight a war on two

173

fronts, one on the continent of Europe, and the other in the Pacific Ocean.

For years Johnson had been a member of the Naval Reserve. One hour after our country declared war on Japan, he asked to be called up for active duty, and became the first member of Congress to don a uniform for service.

He served aboard ship as Lieutenant Commander with our naval forces in the Pacific. Later he served as a special envoy for President Roosevelt to New Zealand and Australia. At the end of the war, he was awarded the Silver Star for meritorious service.

In 1948, when he still was only forty years old, he was elected to the United States Senate. Now the prediction, which Grandpa Johnson had made about him years before, had come true. His mother, who was still living, was extremely proud and happy.

In the United States Senate, Johnson rapidly

rose to a position of leadership. Almost immediately he was appointed to the important Armed Services Committee, which wielded great influence in shaping foreign affairs.

In 1951, when the Democratic senators controlled the Senate, they elected him Democratic whip. In this position he served directly under the Majority Leader and became the second most powerful man in the Senate.

In 1953, when the Republican senators controlled the Senate, the Democratic senators elected him Minority Leader, or their official spokesman. Two years later, when the Democratic senators again controlled the Senate, they elected him Majority Leader. Now, without question, he was considered one of the most powerful political figures in the country.

In 1958 and 1959, while he was serving as Majority Leader, he delivered two "State of the Union" addresses to his Democratic colleagues in the Senate. In these important addresses he called upon Congress to pass certain legislation which he felt was urgently needed at the time. He asked for specific bills to deal with civil rights, poverty, and crime and for other legislation to strengthen our national defenses and to promote the exploration of outer space. His addresses had great influence on Congress.

As Majority Leader, he demonstrated extraordinary ability to get senatorial action on bills. In the fall of 1959, he obtained action on 156 different bills, which members of Congress had introduced. He insisted that the Senate take action on these bills before it adjourned for the holiday season.

In the presidential election of 1960, several prominent Democrats, including Johnson, campaigned for the party nomination for President. At the Democratic National Convention, John F. Kennedy was chosen as the party candidate.

Kennedy, in turn, selected Johnson to be his running mate as the candidate for Vice-President. The opposing Republican candidate for President was Richard M. Nixon, who had been Vice-President under President Dwight D. Eisenhower for eight years.

At this time the country was enjoying business prosperity but was suffering from widespread dissatisfaction, racial disorder, and crime. Kennedy and Johnson put on a strenuous campaign, explaining some of the steps they planned to take to improve these conditions. They won the election in November and were inaugurated, January 20, 1961.

In his inaugural address, President Kennedy set forth a new program, which he called, "The New Frontier," to solve many social problems and bring about better living conditions. He explained that this new program would require much new legislation by Congress and many

177

years of intensive effort. He concluded his appeal by calling for immediate action with this slogan, "But Let Us Begin."

In announcing his new program, Kennedy called for close cooperation. He paid high tribute to Johnson and announced that he planned to rely heavily on him for assistance and advice. The two of them would combine their efforts to work together as a team.

Soon after Kennedy took office, he sent Johnson on goodwill and fact-finding trips to foreign countries in many parts of the world. On these extensive trips Johnson visited fifty-three countries and traveled approximately 120,000 miles, or a distance equivalent to five times around the earth. In many cases, he was accompanied by his wife Lady Bird and their two daughters Linda and Luci.

A President
of Action

PRESIDENT JOHN F. KENNEDY worked very hard to put across his program, "The New Frontier." He asked Congress to pass many new laws to make it succeed. He traveled to many parts of the country to make speeches about it and to explain it to the people.

On November 22, 1963, he was scheduled to make a morning address in Fort Worth, Texas, and afterwards to participate in a noonday parade and to deliver an address in nearby Dallas. In planning this trip, he arranged for his wife Jacqueline and Vice-President Johnson and his wife Lady Bird to accompany him.

As per schedule, the Kennedys and the Johnsons flew to Love Field in Texas on an Air Force jet airplane. President Kennedy delivered his morning address in Fort Worth and headed happily for Dallas. Little did he realize that his hours were numbered.

While he and his wife were headed downtown in an open automobile in Dallas, he was shot by an assassin hiding in a building. He was rushed to a nearby hospital, but never regained consciousness. Fortunately for Vice-President Johnson, he and his wife were riding in a different automobile.

Immediately arrangements were made for Vice-President Johnson to be sworn in as President. The ceremony was held aboard the same Air Force jet airplane which had brought him to Texas. His wife, Lady Bird, and President Kennedy's widow, Jacqueline, shaken with grief, witnessed the ceremony.

At first President Johnson was too stunned to make a public statement. After he reached Washington, however, he spoke to the American people by television and radio. In this brief address, he humbly called for help from the people and from God.

As President, Johnson moved quickly to lessen the shock of Kennedy's death. He invited all of Kennedy's cabinet members to retain their positions. He addressed a joint session of Congress with members of the Supreme Court and the President's cabinet invited to be present. This address was broadcast to all parts of the country and to many parts of the world.

In this address, President Johnson stated that he expected to continue President Kennedy's policies and programs. He referred to the slogan which Kennedy had proclaimed, "But Let Us Begin." Then he announced that as President his slogan would be, "Let Us Continue."

From the beginning, President Johnson felt gravely responsible for the welfare of people in everyday life. Somehow he wanted to help them to have better living conditions with fewer worries, burdens, and problems. In looking to the future, he called for the formation of a "Great Society," in which far more people could be successful and happy. This "Great Society" became his hope for the future.

In January, 1964, in his first Presidential "State of the Union" address to Congress, he asked for the passage of much legislation for public welfare. "Let this session of Congress be known as the session which did more for Civil rights than the last one hundred sessions combined," he exclaimed. "Let it be known as the session which helped to build more houses and more schools and more libraries and more hospitals than any single session of Congress in the history of the Republic."

Following this urgent appeal on the part of President Johnson, Congress cooperated in passing numerous bills which he requested. Most of these bills dealt with such issues as civil rights, education, health, social security, poverty, public housing, labor relations, and foreign relations. Altogether this session of Congress passed more laws than any other session of Congress in the entire history of the country except in the early '30's during the depression.

When Johnson became President, he inherited a commitment which eventually involved us in war in Southeast Asia. Several small independent countries in this area were in grave danger of being taken over by Communists. In 1954, our country, under the leadership of President Dwight D. Eisenhower, had signed a treaty, called the Southeast Asia Collective Defense Treaty, designed to protect small countries in this area from aggression.

For a few years this treaty had seemed to work fairly well, but gradually Communists had secretly worked their way into several small countries, principally South Vietnam, and had begun to cause trouble. Most of them had come from North Vietnam, which had received encouragement and aid from Communist China and the Soviet Union.

Our country, after signing the treaty, had attempted to help South Vietnam and the other small independent countries build up enough strength to fight aggression by themselves. We even had sent military supplies and technical advisers to help them. By 1964, however, during Johnson's first year as President, so many Communists had infiltrated South Vietnam and a few other countries that serious trouble could erupt at almost any moment.

Finally in 1964, North Vietnam torpedo boats attacked some of our warships off the coast of

North Vietnam. In retaliation, President Johnson ordered our airplanes to bomb the torpedo boat bases. Next, we landed troops to help protect South Vietnam and began to engage in open warfare with North Vietnam. President Johnson felt impelled to take this action to uphold the treaty which we had signed nine years before.

This war was destined to drag on for many years and to become very costly, both in lives and money. North Vietnam received more and more aid from China and the Soviet Union, and we sent hundreds of thousands of troops to South Vietnam. All the while our navy patrolled the nearby waters and our airplanes bombed the military bases in North Vietnam. President Johnson repeatedly tried to make peace, but North Vietnam refused.

One of Johnson's greatest contributions as President was his arduous attempt to set up a strong outer space and missile program. In

1957, while Majority Leader of the Senate, he had been greatly disturbed when the Soviet Union had announced the development of a ballistic missile which it could send through outer space to other continents. Later that same year, he had been still more disturbed when the Soviet Union had launched a satellite, called Sputnik, into outer space to encircle the earth. The Soviet Union now held technological space leadership which could prove extremely dangerous to the rest of the world.

In 1958, as Majority Leader, Johnson had brought about the passage of the National Aeronautics and Space Administration Act. At first, this program had been limited primarily to research, but in the early 1960's our country had begun to launch men into outer space and to encircle the earth in outer space. Then in 1964, during Johnson's first year as President, we launched our first successful ballistic missile.

By now we had overtaken the Soviet Union in space and missile achievements, and within a few years would be the first country to land men on the moon. Today, because of Johnson's early leadership, he often is considered the father of our space and missile program.

In 1964, President Johnson was unanimously nominated by the National Democratic Convention to run for a full term as President. His running mate and candidate for Vice-President was Hubert H. Humphrey, United States Senator from Minnesota. In November, they were elected by an overwhelming vote.

At once, following his election to a full four-year term, Johnson began to press Congress for more legislation to promote his Great Society. One of his most notable measures was a bill to establish a form of Federal insurance for the aged, called Medicare. This insurance has brought relief to millions of persons.

While Johnson was President, he and his family made frequent weekend visits to their ranch in the Hill Country of Texas. In 1951, he had purchased this ranch in his old boyhood community and named it the "LBJ Ranch." Often he took important guests with him, as rulers or ambassadors from other countries. At other times he took members of his cabinet or members of Congress to help him carry on work.

In 1968, he announced that he would not be a candidate for re-election. Many prominent persons urged him to reconsider, but he insisted that after spending over half of his life in government service, he was in dire need of rest. Besides he felt that he should turn over the leadership to somebody else.

The following January, when his term expired, the members of his cabinet presented him with a scroll bearing the title, "Landmark Laws of the Lyndon B. Johnson Administration." Directly beneath this heading was the statement, "With these acts President Lyndon B. Johnson and the Congress wrote a record of hope and opportunity for America." Then followed the names of 207 acts, listed by years, which Congress had passed, mostly at his request.

In January, 1969, Johnson and his wife Lady Bird moved permanently to the LBJ Ranch. By now their two daughters had married and had families of their own. The entire group had many happy gatherings at the ranch.

Almost immediately after Johnson retired, he started to work on a book, *The Vantage Point: Perspectives of the Presidency, 1963-1969*, which was published in 1971. This book told the story of exciting incidents that had taken place during his administration.

Early in his retirement he also supervised construction of the LBJ Library, which was built on the campus of the University of Texas at Austin. This enormous structure was built to preserve official records which he had accumulated during his many years in Washington. Altogether it houses approximately thirty-one million documents.

Johnson's chief means of relaxation came from making repairs on his ranch. Often he could be seen dressed in work clothes doing odd jobs here and there. He personally helped to construct an irrigation system for the ranch, using water from the Pedernales River. He spent much time riding horseback to look after and inspect his herds of cattle.

Unfortunately Johnson's retirement lasted only about four years. During much of this time he suffered ill health, which prevented him from carrying out many of his plans. Always, however, he tried to conceal his suffering in the presence of his family and friends because he wanted them to be happy.

In December, 1972, Johnson looked forward eagerly to Christmas and New Year's. During the holidays he and Lady Bird entertained their two daughters and their families. This happy family gathering turned out to be the last he ever would enjoy. From then on, he failed rapidly, had several severe attacks, and died January 22, 1973.

Lyndon B. Johnson was buried beside his parents and grandparents in the simple family cemetery on the LBJ Ranch. He had risen to the greatest possible heights of leadership and had served his country long and well.

More About This Book

WHEN LYNDON B. JOHNSON LIVED

1908   LYNDON JOHNSON WAS BORN IN THE HILL COUNTRY OF TEXAS, AUGUST 17.

There were forty-six states in the Union.

Theodore Roosevelt was President.

The population of the country was about 88,780,000.

1908–
1927   LYNDON GREW UP, GRADUATED FROM HIGH SCHOOL, AND HELD SEVERAL JOBS.

Robert Peary discovered the North Pole, 1909.

The Panama Canal was completed and opened to traffic, 1914.

World War I was fought, 1914–1918.

The League of Nations was formed, 1920.

Women in the United States received the right to vote, 1920.

President Warren G. Harding died, and Calvin Coolidge became President, 1923.

Charles A. Lindbergh flew a small airplane across the Atlantic Ocean, 1927.

1927– JOHNSON ATTENDED COLLEGE, TAUGHT
1937   SCHOOL, AND ENTERED POLITICS.

The first full-length talking motion picture was made in 1927.

Stock market prices crashed and a severe depression followed, 1929.

Wiley Post flew a small airplane around the world, 1933.

1937– JOHNSON SERVED AS U. S. REPRESENTATIVE
1961   AND SENATOR, AND IN WORLD WAR II.

World War II was fought, 1939–1945.

Our country dropped atomic bombs on Hiroshima and Nagasaki, Japan, 1945.

The United Nations Charter was adopted, 1945.

The Korean War was fought, 1950–1953.

1961– JOHNSON BECAME VICE-PRESIDENT AND PRESI-
1973   DENT, AND AFTERWARDS RETIRED.

President Kennedy was assassinated in Dallas, Texas, 1963.

Congress passed numerous laws to improve standards of living, 1964–1968.

North Vietnam torpedoed a U. S. ship, causing the Vietnam War, 1964.

1973   LYNDON B. JOHNSON DIED AT HIS TEXAS RANCH, JANUARY 22.

There were fifty states in the Union.

Richard M. Nixon was President.

The population of the country was about 208,440,000.

DO YOU REMEMBER?

1. How did Lyndon sometimes earn an apple when he went to see Grandpa Johnson?

2. Why did Lyndon's parents decide to enroll him in a Saturday dancing class?

3. How did Lyndon manage to conquer the stubborn Mexican burro?

4. What happened to Lyndon and Tom when they attempted to baptize Otto?

5. How did Lyndon advertise for business as a shoe-shine boy?

6. How did Lyndon obtain a summer job of herding goats on a ranch?

7. How did Lyndon help his father campaign for re-election as a state representative?

8. Why did Lyndon's father appoint him straw boss to look after the chores?

9. What did Lyndon see and do when he visited the state legislature?

10. Why did the boys lose out to the girls in the cotton picking contest?

11. What exciting stories from history did Lyndon recall when he visited the Alamo?

12. Why did Lyndon work rather than go to college after graduating from high school?

13. How did Lyndon distinguish himself as a student in college?

14. What important positions did Johnson hold on his way up to Vice-President?

15. What were Johnson's leading achievements during his years as President?

IT'S FUN TO LOOK UP THESE THINGS

1. Why is the Alamo looked upon as a shrine by the people of Texas?

2. What determines whether a Senate Majority Leader is a Democrat or a Republican?

3. When does a President usually deliver a State of the Union Message to Congress?

4. What are the regular duties and responsibilities of a Vice-President?

5. What benefits for people did Johnson hope to secure under his "Great Society"?

6. How was the United States obligated to go to the rescue of South Vietnam?

INTERESTING THINGS YOU CAN DO

1. Draw a map of Texas and mark the approximate location where Johnson grew up.

2. Prepare a report on the history of Texas up to the time it became a state.

3. Read to find out more about Sam Houston and his early contributions to Texas.

4. Make a list of Vice-Presidents who have succeeded Presidents dying in office.

5. Find out how many members there are in the Senate and House of Representatives.

6. Collect photographs of Johnson for an exhibit on the bulletin board.

OTHER BOOKS YOU MAY ENJOY READING

America and Its Presidents, Earl S. Miers. Grosset.

Harry S. Truman: Missouri Farm Boy, Wilma J. Hudson. Trade and School Editions, Bobbs-Merrill.

Heroes of Texas, Edward Allen. Messner.

John F. Kennedy: Young Statesman, Lucy Post Frisbee. Trade and School Editions, Bobbs-Merrill.

Lyndon Baines Johnson, Helen D. Olds. Putnam.

Stars Over Texas, Carolyn Adams. Naylor.

When Cowboys Rode the Chisholm Trail, James McCague. Garrard.

INTERESTING WORDS IN THIS BOOK

anticipate (ăn tĭs′ĭ pāt) : foresee

ballistic (bă lĭs′tĭk) : possessing characteristics for being fired or hurled into space

congregate (kŏng′grė gāt) : gather together, form a crowd

consecutive (kŏn sĕk′ů tĭv) : following one after another without break

defiance (dė fī′ăns) : resistance to power, standing up to authority

demonstration (dĕm′ŭn strā′shŭn) : show to exhibit or explain something

dense (dĕns) : thick, growing close together

determination (dĕ tûr′mĭ nā′shŭn) : firmness of purpose

dilapidated (dĭ lăp′ĭ dāt′ĕd) : aged and weather-beaten, falling to pieces

dire (dīr) : extreme

envoy (ĕn′voi) : messenger or representative of a ruler or government

gourd (gōrd) : fruit of a plant, somewhat like a pumpkin, often hollowed out and used as a container

hallowed (hăl′ōd) : holy or sacred

infiltrate (ĭn fĭl′trāt) : pass through or into at various weak points

irritated (ĭr′ĭ tāt′ĕd) : annoyed

issue (ĭsh′ōō) : problem, question or point to be debated

katydid (kā′tĭ dĭd′) : large green insect related to the grasshopper

lambaste (lăm bāst′) : criticise severely

lurch (lûrch) : lean or roll suddenly to one side

massacre (măs'à kĕr) : kill large numbers of helpless or defenseless persons

penitentiary (pĕn' tĕn'shà rĭ) : prison

persistent (pẽr sĭs'tĕnt) : continuing regardless of obstacles

prominent (prŏm'ĭ nĕnt) : important, leading, outstanding

revise (rẻ vīz') : alter or change

saunter (sôn'tẽr) : stroll about idly or slowly

siege (sēj) : surrounding a fort or city and cutting it off from the outside world

tuition (tủ ĭsh'ŭn) : money paid for instruction in a school

turmoil (tûr'moil) : commotion, uproar, state of confusion

unanimous (ū năn'ĭ mŭs) : in complete agreement

vengeance (vĕn'jăns) : revenge, great force or violence

weird (wērd) : unearthly, strange, mysterious

whippoorwill (hwĭp'poŏr wĭll') : bird usually seen and heard at twilight or at night

Childhood

OF FAMOUS AMERICANS